D1645456

THE SUN, DANCING

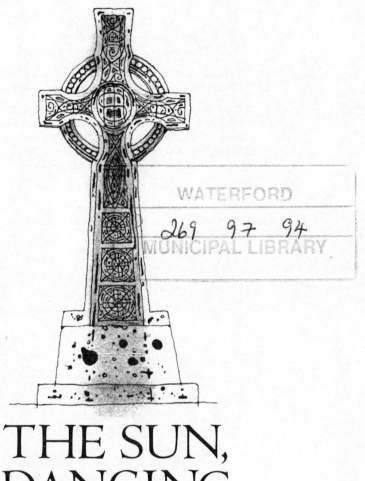

THE SUN, DANCING

CHRISTIAN VERSE

Compiled and Introduced by Charles Causley

Illustrated by Charles Keeping

Kestrel Books

KESTREL BOOKS
Published by Penguin Books Ltd
Harmondsworth, Middlesex, England

First published in 1982

ISBN 0 7226 5593 2
Filmset by Northumberland Press Ltd, Gateshead, Tyne and Wear
Printed in Great Britain by Richard Clay (The Chaucer Press) Ltd,
Bungay, Suffolk

TO MICHAEL HANKE

CONTENTS

ONWARDS FROM EDEN

AFTER THE DREADFUL FLOOD WAS PAST

VOICES AND VISIONS

CHRISTMAS

CONTENTS

CONTENTS

MIRACLES, PARABLES AND MYSTERIES

SAINTS AND PROPHETS

GOD'S CHILDREN

CONTENTS

CONTENTS

INTRODUCTION

It was the seventeenth-century philosopher Thomas Hobbes who declared, 'There are no signes of Religion, but in Man onely.' With the passage of time, the word 'religion', like many another, has acquired additional meanings. Today, to 'make a religion' of something is to carry it to excess. To be described as 'religious' is apt to imply, more often than not, an undue preoccupation with the subject: perhaps even to an extremely sentimental or morbid degree.

But if we accept a definition of 'religion' as that which represents the link between man and God, or the gods, then I think it true to say that all creative activity in the arts is essentially religious in origin: a result of the response by writers, artists and composers to the promptings of that divinely mysterious and wholly undefinable imaginatively creative element within them. Given such a denotation, then, it would be perfectly possible to justify a collection of verse as 'religious' in which no mention of a specific religious belief is made from beginning to end. But the number of world religions is great; their individual literatures vast. An attempt, in a single anthology, to represent them at all adequately would seem to me to promise nothing more than a dilution of effect. *The Sun, Dancing*, then, is confined simply to a particular segment of religious belief. I see the poems I have chosen to have been written basically from a Christian standpoint, or to embody a Christian point of view.

I make no suggestion, of course, that the ideas, principles and attitudes expressed in many of the poems are exclusively Christian. Nor – faced by the great and ever-increasing store of Christian literature – do I claim that the selection is a comprehensive one. It remains an entirely personal choice. I have tried to bear in mind that the word 'anthology' springs from a Greek root: *anthologia*, meaning a collection or gather-

15

ing of flowers – an occupation equally as personal, and perhaps as self-revealing.

In the selection, myth, legend, speculation and plain fact are intermixed. What is of the greatest value here is poetic truth: something, hopefully, ever more salutary and meaningful as we reflect on the mysteries of human existence than a mere recital of factual evidence. This is only one reason why I have chosen to begin with the lines sometimes attributed to Amergin, a legendary poet (probably about as 'real' as Merlin) of the invading Sons of Mil, ancestors of the Gaels, and said to have been spoken by him when he first set his right foot on the soil of Ireland.

I also felt it essential that such an anthology should be as wide-ranging as possible, embracing many contrasting forms and styles. The mystical and mysterious poem of Amergin has, significantly, the line, 'I am the point of the lance in battle'. The Australian poet Geoff Page with his *Christ at Gallipoli* shocks the sensibilities almost like a shell-burst. The setting of the poem is a battle of 1915 that was to be one of the most terrible in world history. But as we probe beneath the surfaces of the two poems, or merely allow them to act upon our imaginations, the image of the earlier warrior-priest-poet of the lance somehow fuses and effects a strange unity with that of Page's Anzac soldier with the 'blood-red bayonet'.

> Bit weird at first,
> That starey look in the eyes,
> The hair down past his shoulders,
> But after a go with the ship's barber,
> A sea-water shower and the old slouch hat
> Across his ears, he started to look the part.   (*page* 213)

R. S. Thomas, himself, as it happens, a priest, presents a marvellously aseptic and unsentimental picture of the Child Jesus in his *Lost Christmas*: three trees on a hill representing the three Kings.

> Pity him. He has come far
> Like the trees, matching their patience
> With his. But the mind was before
> Him on the long road. The manger is empty.　　(*page* 106)

Another present-day poet, D. J. Enright, in *Sunday*, writes with a devastatingly clear eye of his childhood.

> Yet we were sent to Sunday school.
> Perhaps in the spirit that others
> Were sent to public schools. It
> Might come in useful later on.　　(*page* 205)

Not too long ago, perhaps, many poems in the following selection might have been dismissed as heretical, or as wholly unworthy of the description 'Christian'. I think it will be seen, however, that the work of a number of modern (and not so modern) poets shows evidence of a direct and healthy descent from the intimate and cheerful parables of misdemeanour, repentance and forgiveness found in the texts of the medieval miracle plays and in such ballads as *The Maid and the Palmer*.

> She swore by God and good Saint John
> Leman (lover) she had never none.
>
> ... 'Peace, fair maid, you are forsworne,
> Ninè children you have borne.'　　(*page* 175)

The sense of reality and the sudden illumination of common, everyday experience conveyed by ancient poems of this nature is something we may also discover in the work of such a modern poet as Norman Nicholson, in his *A Local Preacher's Goodbye*.

> He pointed to the smoke
> With black umbrella finger
> (The chimneys tall as hymns,
> Fuming with extemporary prayer) –
> 'I'll see you all up there,'
> 　　　　He said.　　(*page* 207)

17

The approach of the American poet Howard Nemerov to his subject in *The Little Aircraft* is rather more oblique, but the poem's inner life and resonance are subtly and surely revealed beneath its deceptively quiet surface.

> The little aircraft trudging through night, cloud, rain,
> Is neither alone nor lost among the great
> Inverted ocean of the air, for a lane
> Invisible gives it intelligence ...   *(page 236)*

Occasionally the same Biblical figure or event reappears in the work of writers of greatly differing method. The anonymous author of the excerpt from the Chester Cycle of miracle plays, for example, in a thrilling verse-alternative to the original Bible story, presents an intensely dramatic theatre-piece. Wilfred Owen, killed in France in his twenty-fifth year and only a week before the Armistice of 1918, in his *The Parable of the Old Man and the Young* (page 212) changes, to dreadful effect, the ending of this famous story and produces one of the most profoundly moving poems of war in the language.

It is vital, always, to remember the many faces, many aspects of what may at first appear the most simple-seeming poem. The German parents of Karen Gershon died in Hitler's concentration camps. There is, then, an awesome duality in such a poem as *That Night*, in which the poet may at first appear to be writing only of the Children of Israel awaiting their summons to leave the land of Egypt.

> That night they waited shut inside their houses,
> fully dressed and their belongings packed;
> small children lay where sleep had caught them up,
> older ones watched their parents being afraid.   *(page 66)*

When considering the story of Lot's wife as she quits the wicked city, the same poet totally transforms for us that traditionally rather unsympathetic figure. It is an unforgettable moment.

My home, my lovely home, she wept
while God was sharpening his shafts
against the cities of the plain.
My mother too was called at dawn
and for me Lot's wife has her face,
the same companionable hands
touch what they shall not hold again ...   (*page* 59)

Quite apart from its purely literary quality, the range of religious verse produced over almost a thousand years tells us much about the subtly changing pattern of Christian belief. The inner strengths of that belief seem to me to be even more clearly demonstrated by its capacity to absorb and thrive on fresh attitudes and on excitingly varied interpretations of religious thought and experience. In the writing of religious verse, too, it is clear that the poet has at times felt deprived of what might be thought a great essential: the opportunity of adopting a purely personal tone. In speaking of man's relationship with God, it was often assumed by the writer that an entirely elevated tone was demanded. Yet time and again, through the ages, the poets show us in fascinating variety how they ignored, accepted, or wrestled with this particular problem: whether with the stark simplicity of the medieval balladeer or with the seventeenth-century George Herbert's delicate representations of Jesus as an intimate and personal reality; through the imposingly noble and organ-like tones of Milton or in the fresh and bright colourings of thought and feeling – child-like but never childish – employed by Roy Campbell in *Mass at Dawn*.

My boat in her new paint shone like a bride,
And silver in my baskets shone the bream:
My arms were tired and I was heavy-eyed,
But when with food and drink, at morning-light,
The children met me at the water-side,
Never was wine so red or bread so white.   (*page* 220)

For me, as a child, the most important religious festival

19

in the year was Christmas. Now I know that the emphasis should rather be on what Robert Herrick in *Candlemas Eve* (page 129) calls 'the dancing Easter Day'. There is, certainly, an ancient legend that on Easter Day the sun danced. This suggested itself to me, irresistibly, as the basis of a title for the present collection. Does the sun dance on Easter Day? I hope that the poetic truths contained in the poems that follow may give their own answer.

Launceston, Cornwall   CHARLES CAUSLEY

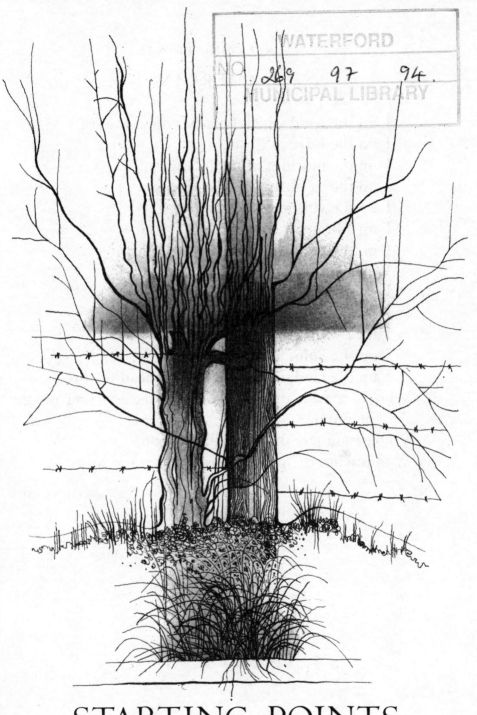

STARTING POINTS

AMERGIN

I am the wind which breathes upon the sea,
I am the wave of the ocean,
I am the murmur of the billows,
I am the ox of the seven combats,
I am the vulture upon the rocks,
I am a beam of the sun,
I am the fairest of plants,
I am a wild boar in valour,
I am a salmon in the water,
I am a lake in the plain,
I am a word of science,
I am the point of the lance in battle,
I am the God who creates in the head the fire.
Who is it who throws light into the meeting on the
    mountain?
Who announces the ages of the moon?
Who teaches the place where couches the sun?

ANONYMOUS

FLOWER IN THE CRANNIED WALL

Flower in the crannied wall,
I pluck you out of the crannies; –
Hold you here, root and all, in my hand,
Little flower – but if I could understand
What you are, root and all, and all in all,
I should know what God and man is.

ALFRED, LORD TENNYSON

PRESENCE

Expecting Him, my door was open wide:
Then I looked round
If any lack of service might be found,
And saw Him at my side:
How entered, by what secret stair,
I know not, knowing only He was there.

T. E. BROWN

LOST AND FOUND

I missed him when the sun began to bend;
I found him not when I had lost his rim;
With many tears I went in search of him,
Climbing high mountains which did still ascend,
And gave me echoes when I called my friend;

Through cities vast and charnel-houses grim,
And high cathedrals where the light was dim,
Through books and arts and works without an end,
But found him not – the friend whom I had lost.
And yet I found him – as I found the lark,
A sound in fields I heard but could not mark;
I found him nearest when I missed him most;
I found him in my heart, a life in frost,
A light I knew not till my soul was dark.

GEORGE MACDONALD

SAID THE STRAW

'It's the last camel,' said the straw,
'The last camel that breaks our backs.'

'Consider the lilies,' he said,
'How they toil in the fields.
Six days they labour,
On Sunday they wear their best clothes.'

'Ask why the violet sickened,
The pale primrose died unmarried,
And the daisy lies in chains,'
He said, 'All grass is flesh.'

'But let us hear no more,'
So said the straw,
'About the sorrows of the camel
With its huge and heavy feet.'

D. J. ENRIGHT

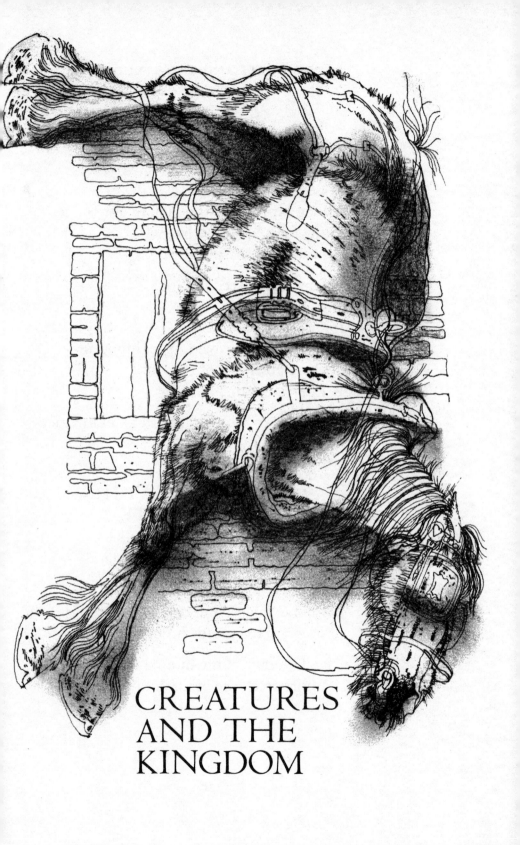

CREATURES
AND THE
KINGDOM

THE EXILE

The fool said to the animals:
'You are merely my chattels,
With one lesson to learn –
That what happens to you is not your concern
But mine; for a just God has set
You on earth for my profit.'

The animals answered the fool
Nothing at all,
But for a single moment
Turned on him their wild, true, innocent
Eyes, where an Angel of the Lord
Holds Eden's flaming sword.

FRANCES BELLERBY

A DOG STARVED AT HIS
MASTER'S GATE

A dog starved at his master's gate
Predicts the ruin of the State.

A horse misused upon the road
Cries to Heaven for human blood.

Each outcry of the hunted hare
A fibre from the brain does tear.

Kill not the moth nor butterfly;
For the Last Judgment draweth nigh.

WILLIAM BLAKE

BEYOND THE HEADLINES

Then I saw the wild geese flying
In fair formation to their bases in Inchicore
And I knew that these wings would outwear the wings of
    war
And a man's simple thoughts outlive the day's loud
    lying.
Don't fear, don't fear, I said to my soul.
The Bedlam of Time is an empty bucket rattled,
'Tis you who will say in the end who best battles.
Only they who fly home to God have flown at all.

PATRICK KAVANAGH

HERON

Flaps a way north
Across a strong north-easterly,
Making the best of unwieldy wings
Like huge grey sails.

Driven by some wind of his own
Against the trend of the weather.

Gusts catch him now and again
But he is determined,
Though these are blunt weapons
For cutting this kind of air.

Imagine a tall ship
Moving whole masts and yards,
A Heath Robinson contraption
With beating sails! I reckon
Such things must astonish God.

JOHN NORMANTON

W. Heath Robinson (1872 – 1944) was an artist whose comic drawings were often of apparently quite functionable machines made up of ridiculous working-parts (items of furniture, brooms, umbrellas, etc.).

THE WICKED PIG

(*Air: 'Go to the Devil and Shake Yourself'*)

Merciful powers, will ye look at this villain,
The worst that the divil has ever employed.
Never his like for devourin' and killin';
Night, noon and morning he has me destroyed.
Six of me chickens he's eaten, the brute,
And chawed up the breeches of Peter's new suit;
Desperate animal, murdering cannibal,
Where is the happiness once I enjoyed?

That pig is devisin' whatever he pleases,
There's none can control him or keep him in hand.
He rules us and rules us. O merciful Jesus,
Tell me the thing that I can't understand.
'Twas yourself that imprisoned the divil in swine,
And we in our trespasses dare not repine.
We have to go through it – but, why did ye do it?
What made ye give such a drastic command?

L. A. G. STRONG

A DREAM OF NATURE

Birds I saw in bushes made nests.
Even a simple one no man
Could ever make. And when and where
I wondered did the magpie learn
To weave sticks one with another
To secure her nest? Carpenters
Couldn't do anything as good,
No designer make a blueprint
For it either. It astonished
Me even more that many birds
Hid their eggs, carefully concealed,
So that only the parent birds
Themselves could find them. Some I saw
Did their breeding high in the trees
And hatched their young way up above
The ground. Diving birds plumped deep down
In swamps, moorland ponds and reedbeds,

Wherever there was water. 'Dear
God,' I cried, 'What school do all these
Wild things go to, to get such sense?'
And then the peacock; I saw how
He mated, how roughly the bird
Went about it. I marvelled at
His splendour along with his crude
Screaming voice. I looked at the sea
And on further to the high stars.
The whole world was full of wonders
Too many to put down now, flowers
In the fields, their dazzling colours,
So many different shades, sprung
From the same earth and grassy fields,
Some bitter to the taste, some sweet.
It seemed all one great miracle
Ranged too wide for me to record.
But what struck me and set me back
Was that reason seemed to govern
All creatures and how they acted
Except for man, except mankind.

WILLIAM LANGLAND
(from *The Vision of Piers Plowman*,
translated from the Middle English
by Ronald Tamplin)

PRAYERS AND SONGS

GRACE FOR CHILDREN

What God gives, and what we take,
'Tis a gift for Christ his sake:
Be the meal of beans and peas,
God be thank'd for those, and these:
Have we flesh, or have we fish.
All are fragments from his dish.
He his church save, and the king,
And our peace here, like a spring,
Make it ever flourishing.

ROBERT HERRICK

THE HUNDRED AND THIRTY-SEVENTH PSALM PARAPHRASED

(*To the tune of 'The Shandon Bells'*)

By foreign waters
Zion's sons and daughters
Have taken up quarters
   Through mischance so deep;
Where the Tigris in spate is,
Likewise the Euphrates,
Our cruel fate is
   To sit and weep.

Remembering Zion,
The harps we play on
In the weeping willows
   We did them hang,

When Nebuchadnezzar
And Tiglath Pileser,
All for to ease them,
   Were asking a song.

The psalms of David
When the Lord he praises,
Likewise of Asaph
   And Solomon –
How can we sing them
Or to memory bring them
By the Hanging Gardens
   Of Babylon?

May my senses wander
And my right hand blunder
If I do not remember
   The dear hills of home;
My tongue turn rotten
And my teeth be dropping
When I am forgetting
   Jerusalem.

O Lord, take heed of
The children of Edom,
Destroying our freedom
   And the darling town;
With 'Raze it, raze it,'
They did dispraise it,
In our troublesome days it
   Was 'Pluck it down!'

And I hope 'twill bring trouble on
The girls of Babylon

That dip and dabble on
These streams so fair,
But it's I would be blessing
The man who was dashing
Their little children
On the sharp stones there.

JOHN HEATH-STUBBS

Tiglath Pileser: Assyrian king (reigned 744–727 B.C.) who also ruled Syria
and Palestine, and in 729 B.C. merged the kingdoms of Babylon and
Assyria in his own person
Asaph: a Levite, dedicated to religious service, who had been appointed
leader of King David's choir

BY THE RIVERS OF BABYLON WE SAT DOWN AND WEPT

We sat down and wept by the waters
Of Babel, and thought of the day
When our foe, in the hue of his slaughters,
Made Salem's high places his prey;
And ye, oh her desolate daughters!
Were scatter'd all weeping away.

While sadly we gazed on the river
Which roll'd on in freedom below,
They demanded the song; but, oh never
That triumph the stranger shall know!
May this right hand be wither'd for ever,
Ere it string our high harp for the foe!

On the willow that harp is suspended,
   Oh Salem! its sound should be free;
And the hour when thy glories were ended
   But left me that token of thee:
And ne'er shall its soft tones be blended
   With the voice of the spoiler by me!

GEORGE GORDON, LORD BYRON

ST PATRICK'S HYMN BEFORE TARA

   Christ, as a light,
   Illumine and guide me!
Christ, as a shield, o'ershadow and cover me!
Christ be under me! Christ be over me!
   Christ be beside me
   On left hand and right!
Christ be before me, behind me, about me!
Christ this day be within and without me!

Christ, the lowly and meek,
   Christ, the All-powerful, be
In the heart of each to whom I speak,
   In the mouth of each who speaks to me!
     In all who draw near me,
     Or see me or hear me!

At Tara to-day, in this awful hour,
   I call on the Holy Trinity!
Glory to Him who reigneth in power,
The God of the Elements, Father, and Son,
And Paraclete Spirit, which Three are the One,
   The ever-existing Divinity!

Salvation dwells with the Lord,
With Christ, the Omnipotent Word.
From generation to generation
Grant us, O Lord, Thy grace and salvation!

JAMES CLARENCE MANGAN
(from the Irish)

Paraclete: name given to the Holy Ghost, or 'Comforter'; see St John,
Ch. 14: vv 16 and 26

GLORIOUS THE SUN IN MID CAREER

Glorious the sun in mid career;
Glorious th' assembled fires appear;
   Glorious the comet's train:
Glorious the trumpet and alarm;
Glorious th' Almighty's stretched-out arm;
   Glorious th' enraptured main:

Glorious the northern lights a-stream;
Glorious the song, when God's the theme;
   Glorious the thunder's roar:
Glorious Hosanna from the den;
Glorious the catholic Amen;
   Glorious the martyr's gore:

Glorious, – more glorious – is the crown
Of Him that brought salvation down,
   By meekness called thy Son:
Thou that stupendous truth believed; –
And now the matchless deed's achieved,
   DETERMINED, DARED and DONE!

CHRISTOPHER SMART
(from *A Song to David*)

THE STORM PETREL

Far out at sea, a little dark bird,
No bigger than a sparrow. It teeters over the waves,
The troughs and crests, paddling with its feet,
Seeming to walk like Peter
Upon Gennasaret.

Is it a land bird that has lost its way? No,
But this is Mother Carey's chicken,
Harbinger of the storm.

O Mother Carey, green-toothed hag,
Mistress of the hurricane, your herds
The mighty choirs of singing whales, be lenient
To sailors and trawlermen, all who ply their way
Through dirty weather, over the hungry deep.

JOHN HEATH-STUBBS

Gennasaret: Sea of Galilee
Mother Carey: originally, probably a corruption by sailors of *madre cara*
  or *mater cara*; the 'mother dear' being the Virgin Mary

THE HOUSE SPARROW

Citizen Philip Sparrow, who likes
To build and breed about our habitations –
   The little birds that fly through the city smoke –

Prolific, adaptable, bold,
Untidy, cheerfully vocal –
   The little birds that quarrel in the eaves –

Grant him his right of freedom and, of your charity,
His dole of crumbs and kitchen scraps –
   The little birds that stand in the eye of God.

JOHN HEATH-STUBBS

Philip Sparrow: a deliberate echo from 'The Sparrow's Dirge', a poem by
John Skelton (1460?–1529), in which Philip, a pet sparrow, is killed by
a cat

THE RAIN

Rain, do not hurt my flowers, but quickly spread
Your honey drops: presse not to smell them here:
When they are ripe, their odour will ascend
And at your lodging with their thanks appear.

GEORGE HERBERT

THE PRAYER OF DAFT HARRY

Lord, since this world is filled with fire,
    Inside this rounded mould –
Let's turn it inside out, O Lord,
    While hands and feet are cold.

Let's split the world in half, O Lord,
    As open as my palm,
Until the snow has melted down,
    And hands and feet are warm.

Let's turn the world all inside out,
    And glorify Our Name;
Until Our fire makes Jesus laugh,
    While I blow up the flame.

Let's do it now, this minute, Lord,
    And make a glorious blaze:
Till Jesus laughs and claps his hands,
    While Mary sings Our praise!

W. H. DAVIES

CAROL

On Friday in the shopping crowd
the fiddler man with bony arms
made a song from string and wood
that sounded like the stars aloud
and Friday people from the farms
and loungers pocketing their thumbs
stopped to hear the theme he played.

39

Outside the bank the beggar man
stood in the gutter of the street
and made his mortal music turn
into a testament as plain
and fine and wise as bread, as sweet
as liniment on tired feet,
and terrible and true as wine.

His hair clenched round his head in thorns,
he wore it like a sign of love,
but when the brave boys threw him stones
and broke his prince of violins
he slowly packed his case to leave,
and we had neither coins to give
nor thanks to tell him for his pains.

THOMAS W. SHAPCOTT

A CHILD'S EVENING PRAYER

Ere on my bed my limbs I lay,
God grant me grace my prayers to say:
O God! preserve my mother dear
In strength and health for many a year;
And, O! preserve my father too,
And may I pay him reverence due;
And may I my best thoughts employ
To be my parents' hope and joy;
And O! preserve my brothers both
From evil doings and from sloth,
And may we always love each other

Our friends, our father, and our mother:
And still, O Lord, to me impart
An innocent and grateful heart,
That after my great sleep I may
Awake to thy eternal day! Amen.

SAMUEL TAYLOR COLERIDGE

THE SMILE

My mother prayed that I should have the sweet tooth.
My father said that I should have the big fist.
And life, lingering somewhere by,
Smiled on me, giving me neither.

R. S. THOMAS

THE RAIN

The rain it raineth every day,
    Upon the just and unjust fellow,
But more upon the just, because
    The unjust hath the just's umbrella.

ANONYMOUS

THANKSGIVING CAROL

Fields of corn, give up your ears,
Now your ears are heavy,
Wheat and oats and barley spears,
All your harvest levy.

Where your sheaves of plenty lean,
Men once more the grain shall glean
Of the Ever Living,
God the Lord will bless the field,
Bringing in its autumn yield
Gladly to Thanksgiving.

Vines, send in your bunch of grapes,
Now the bunch is clustered,
Be your gold and purple shapes
Round the altar mustered.

Where the hanging bunches shine
Men once more shall taste the wine
Of the Ever Living,
God the Lord will bless the root,
Bringing in its autumn fruit
Gladly to Thanksgiving.

Garden, give your gayest flowers,
Hedge, your wildest bring in,
Turn the churches into bowers
Little birds shall sing in.

Where the children sing their glee
Men once more the Flower shall see
Of the Ever Living,

God the Lord will bless the throng,
Lifting up its autumn song
Gladly in Thanksgiving.

ELEANOR FARJEON
(from the German)

PRAYER

Lord I am not entirely selfish
Lord I am not entirely helpish
O Lord to me be slightly lavish
O Lord be in a minor way lovish

Lord I am not completely bad-mannered
Lord I am not a crusader, mad-bannered
O Lord to me be quite well disposed
O Lord to me be calm and composed

Lord I am not a dog downed and to-heeled
Lord I am not thick about what has been revealed
O Lord you have it in your power to hurt me
O Lord in your odd way please do not desert me

GAVIN EWART

HYMN FOR SATURDAY

Now's the time for mirth and play,
Saturday's an holiday;
Praise to heaven unceasing yield,
I've found a lark's nest in the field.

A lark's nest, then your playmate begs
You'd spare herself and speckled eggs;
Soon she shall ascend and sing
Your praises to the eternal King.

CHRISTOPHER SMART

ONWARDS FROM EDEN

THE CREATION

And God stepped out on space,
And he looked around and said:
I'm lonely –
I'll make me a world.

As far as the eye of God could see
Darkness covered everything,
Blacker than a hundred midnights
Down in a cypress swamp.

Then God smiled,
And the light broke,
And the darkness rolled up on one side,
And the light stood shining on the other,
And God said: That's good!

Then God reached out and took the light in his hands,
And God rolled the light around in his hands
Until he made the sun;
And he set that sun a-blazing in the heavens.
And the light that was left from making the sun
God gathered it up in a shining ball
And flung it against the darkness,
Spangling the night with the moon and stars.
Then down between
The darkness and the light
He hurled the world;
And God said: That's good!

Then God himself stepped down –
And the sun was on his right hand,
And the moon was on his left;

46

The stars were clustered about his head,
And the earth was under his feet.
And God walked, and where he trod
His footsteps hollowed the valleys out
And bulged the mountains up.

Then he stopped and looked and saw
That the earth was hot and barren.
So God stepped over to the edge of the world
And he spat out the seven seas –
He batted his eyes, and the lightnings flashed –
He clapped his hands, and the thunders rolled –
And the waters above the earth came down,
The cooling waters came down.

Then the green grass sprouted,
And the little red flowers blossomed,
The pine tree pointed his finger to the sky,
And the oak spread out his arms,
The lakes cuddled down in the hollows of the ground,
And the rivers ran down to the sea;
And God smiled again,
And the rainbow appeared
And curled itself around his shoulder.

Then God raised his arm and he waved his hand
Over the sea and over the land,
And he said: Bring forth! Bring forth!
And quicker than God could drop his hand,
Fishes and fowls
And beasts and birds
Swam the rivers and the seas,
Roamed the forests and the woods,

And split the air with their wings.
And God said: That's good!

Then God walked around,
And God looked around
On all that he had made.
He looked at his sun,
And he looked at his moon,
And he looked at his little stars;
He looked on his world
With all its living things,
And God said: I'm lonely still.

Then God sat down –
On the side of a hill where he could think;
By a deep, wide river he sat down;
With his head in his hands,
God thought and thought,
Till he thought, I'll make me a man!

Up from the bed of the river
God scooped the clay;
And by the bank of the river
He kneeled him down;
And there the great God Almighty
Who lit the sun and fixed it in the sky,
Who flung the stars to the most far corner of the night,
Who rounded the earth in the middle of his hand;
This great God,
Like a mammy bending over her baby,
Kneeled down in the dust
Toiling over a lump of clay

Till he shaped it in his own image;
Then into it he blew the breath of life,
And man became a living soul.
Amen. Amen.

JAMES WELDON JOHNSON

THEY WONDERED WHY
THE FRUIT HAD BEEN FORBIDDEN

They wondered why the fruit had been forbidden;
It taught them nothing new. They hid their pride,
But did not listen much when they were chidden;
They knew exactly what to do outside.

They left: immediately the memory faded
Of all they'd learnt; they could not understand
The dogs now who, before, had always aided;
The stream was dumb with whom they'd always
    planned.

They wept and quarrelled: freedom was so wild.
In front, maturity, as he ascended,
Retired like a horizon from the child;

The dangers and the punishments grew greater;
And the way back by angels was defended
Against the poet and the legislator.

W. H. AUDEN

49

THE PEACOCK AND THE SNAKE

'It was your fault! It was your fault!' cried the Peacock.
'And it was yours too,' whispered the Snake.

'It was lust! It was lust!' shouted the Peacock.
'Yes, and pride, and vanity,' – so the Snake.

'I loved him! I loved him!' shrieked the Peacock.
'And she was sweet, sweet,' hissed the Snake.

'I look at my feet and I scream' – the Peacock.
'And I have no feet' – the Snake.

'It was your fault!' 'Yours also perhaps?' – thus the
    Peacock-Angel
And the diabolical Snake down in the filthiest pot-hole

Where they exist, reproached each other,
Timeless in their torment. But somewhere

Within the innocent jungle, the peacock (which is a bird)
Displayed beneath the bough a fragment of God's
    splendour;

And the coiled snake (which is a reptile)
Deployed upon the ground a portion of His subtlety.

JOHN HEATH-STUBBS

ANCIENT HISTORY

Adam, a brown old vulture in the rain,
Shivered below his wind-whipped olive-trees;
Huddling sharp chin on scarred and scraggy knees,
He moaned and mumbled to his darkening brain;
'*He was the grandest of them all – was Cain!*
'A lion laired in the hills, that none could tire:
'Swift as a stag: a stallion of the plain,
'Hungry and fierce with deeds of huge desire.'

Grimly he thought of Abel, soft and fair –
A lover with disaster in his face,
And scarlet blossom twisted in bright hair.
'Afraid to fight; was murder more disgrace? ...
'*God always hated Cain*' ... He bowed his head –
The gaunt wild man whose lovely sons were dead.

SIEGFRIED SASSOON

THE HISTORY OF THE FLOOD

Bang Bang Bang
Said the nails in the Ark.

It's getting rather dark
Said the nails in the Ark.

For the rain is coming down
Said the nails in the Ark.

And you're all like to drown
Said the nails in the Ark.

Dark and black as sin
Said the nails in the Ark.

So won't you all come in
Said the nails in the Ark.

But only two by two
Said the nails in the Ark.

So they came in two by two,
The elephant, the kangaroo,
And the gnu,
And the little tiny shrew.

Then the birds
Flocked in like wingèd words:
Two racket-tailed motmots, two macaws,
Two nuthatches and two
Little bright robins.

And the reptiles: the gila monster, the slow-worm,
The green mamba, the cottonmouth, and the alligator –
All squirmed in;
And after a very lengthy walk,
Two giant Galapagos tortoises.

And the insects in their hierarchies:
A queen ant, a king ant, a queen wasp, a king wasp,
A queen bee, a king bee,
And all the beetles, bugs, and mosquitoes,
Cascaded in like glittering, murmurous jewels.

But the fish had their wish;
For the rain came down.
People began to drown:
The wicked, the rich –

They gasped out bubbles of pure gold,
Which exhalations
Rose to the constellations.

So for forty days and forty nights
They were on the waste of waters
In those cramped quarters.
It was very dark, damp, and lonely.
There was nothing to see, but only
The rain which continued to drop.
It did not stop.

So Noah sent forth a raven. The raven said 'Kark!
I will not go back to the Ark.'
The raven was footloose,
He fed on the bodies of the rich –
Rich with vitamins and goo.
They had become bloated,
And everywhere they floated.
The raven's heart was black,
He did not come back.
It was not a nice thing to do:

Which is why the raven is a token of wrath,
And creaks like a rusty gate
When he crosses your path; and Fate
Will grant you no luck that day:
The raven is fey:
You were meant to have a scare.
Fortunately in England
The raven is rather rare.

Then Noah sent forth a dove
She did not want to rove.
She longed for her love –

The other turtle dove –
(For her no other dove!)
She brought back a twig from an olive-tree.
There is no more beautiful tree
Anywhere on the earth,
Even when it comes to birth
From six weeks under the sea.

She did not want to rove.
She wanted to take her rest,
And to build herself a nest
All in the olive grove.
She wanted to make love.
She thought that was the best.

The dove was not a rover;
So they knew that the rain was over.
Noah and his wife got out
(They had become rather stout)
And Japhet, Ham, and Shem.
(The same could be said of them.)
They looked up at the sky.
The earth was becoming dry.

Then the animals came ashore –
There were more of them than before:
There were two dogs and a litter of puppies;
There were a tom-cat and two tib-cats
And two litters of kittens – cats
Do not obey regulations;
And, as you might expect,
A quantity of rabbits.

God put a rainbow in the sky.

They wondered what it was for.
There had never been a rainbow before.
The rainbow was a sign;
It looked like a neon sign –
Seven colours arched in the skies:
What should it publicize?
They looked up with wondering eyes.

It advertises Mercy
Said the nails in the Ark.

Mercy Mercy Mercy
Said the nails in the Ark.

Our God is merciful
Said the nails in the Ark.

Merciful and gracious
Bang Bang Bang Bang.

JOHN HEATH-STUBBS

motmot: bird native to Mexico and South America
gila monster: large, venomous lizard found in S. W. United States (Gila
    River, Arizona) and N. W. Mexico

THE KINGFISHER

When Noah left the Ark, the animals
Capered and gambolled on the squadgy soil,
Enjoying their new-found freedom; and the birds
Soared upwards, twittering, to the open skies.
But one soared higher than the rest, in utter ecstasy,
Till all his back and wings were drenched

With the vivid blue of heaven itself, and his breast
   scorched
With the upward-slanting rays of the setting sun.
When he came back to earth, he had lost the Ark;
His friends were all dispersed. So now he soars no more;
A lonely bird, he darts and dives for fish,
By streams and pools – places where water is –
Still searching, but in vain, for the vanished Ark
And rain-washed terraces of Ararat.

JOHN HEATH-STUBBS

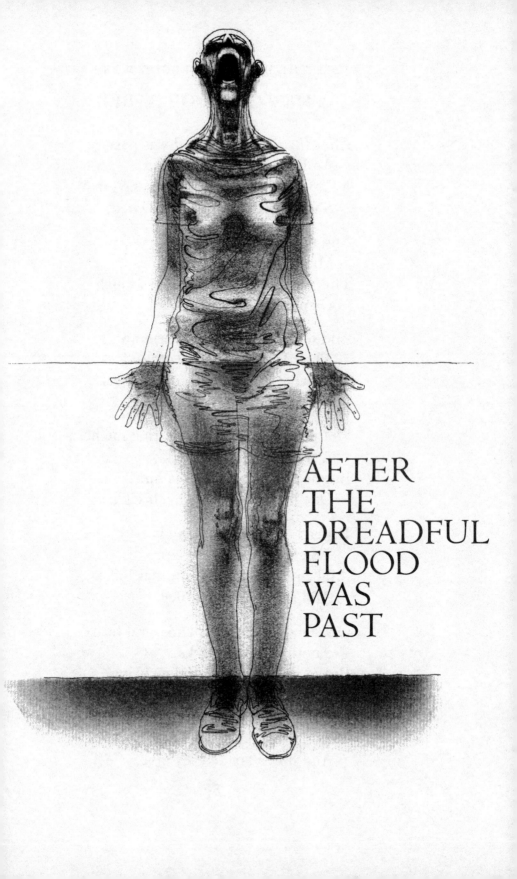

AFTER
THE
DREADFUL
FLOOD
WAS
PAST

THE TOWER OF BABEL

After the dreadful Flood was past,
    And Mankind did abound,
A Tower they built, for fear the earth
    Should once again be drowned,

And that they to posterity
    Might leave a lasting name.
The Almighty saw it and was much
    Displeasèd with the same.

And to prevent this vain attempt,
    Their language did confound
That what they to each other speak
    Was but an empty sound.

So that one cries, 'Come bring me here
    A trowel quickly, quick';
But he a hammer reaches him.
    One he cries, 'Hew this brick';

Instead of which he busy is
    To cleave in two a tree.
'Make fast this rope,' another bids;
    And then they let it flee.

One loudly calls for planks and boards,
    Another mortar lacks;
But to the first a stone they bring,
    And to the last an axe.

One in great haste does nails require,
    And him a spade they give.

Another for a saw doth ask,
   And him they bring a sieve.

Thus being crossly crossed they fret
   And vex but all in vain;
For what one with much pains hath made
   Another spoils again.

This makes them leave their work undone,
   And like mad men, or fools,
They scatter all their stuff abroad,
   And tumble down their tools.

NATHANIEL CROUCH

LOT'S WIFE

I

My home, my lovely home, she wept
while God was sharpening his shafts
against the cities of the plain.
My mother too was called at dawn
and for me Lot's wife has her face,
the same companionable hands
touch what they shall not hold again;
it was because it meant her life
that she was loath to leave that place.

And while her daughters were already running
she stayed to look at a familiar sight:
flowers responding to the early sun
– the valley emulated Paradise;

59

sweet view, she sighed, if I could leave my eyes ...
no one will love you after I have gone.

II

What was she doing, waiting there
with darkness spattering the air;
don't hang your hearts on things, she'd said:
a nomad used to moving on
with only a shabby, a makeshift home
and daughters who still needed her
hurrying ahead?

III

I'd be content with yesterday, she thought,
her memories like clothing in her hands:
her daughters small, herself reckless and young,
and Lot her shelter, and their wanderings.
If God must take, she thought, let him take all ...
and shivered as the ground began to shake.

KAREN GERSHON

O ISAAC, ISAAC, MY DARLING DEAR

ABRAHAM : O Isaac, Isaac, my darling dear,
My blessing now I give thee here.
Take up this faggot with good cheer
And on thy back it bring.
Here the fire with me I take.

ISAAC : Your bidding I will not forsake,
Father, I will never be slack
To fulfil your bidding ...

ABRAHAM : O, my heart will break in three!
To hear thy words I have pity.
As thou wilt, Lord, so must it be
For thee I will obey.

Lay down thy faggot, my own dear son.

ISAAC : All ready, father, look it is here.
But why make you such heavy cheer?
Does anything make you dread?

Father now, if it be your will,
Where is the beast that we shall kill?

ABRAHAM : There is none, son, upon this hill
That I can see to strike dead.

ISAAC : Father, I am full sore afraid
To see your sword thus arrayed.
I hope, by all that is made,
You will not slay your child.

ABRAHAM : My child, I bid thee not dread:
Our Lord will send of his Godhead
Some kind of beast here instead,
Be it tame or wild.

ISAAC : Father, tell me ere I go
Whether I shall be harmed here or no.

ABRAHAM : Ah, dear God, this is such woe
As will burst my heart insunder.

ISAAC : Father, tell me what is amiss,
Why your sword is drawn out like this.
This naked blade frightens me, I wis,
And I am filled with deep wonder.

ABRAHAM : Isaac, son, peace! I pray thee,
Thou breakest my heart quite in three.

ISAAC : I pray you keep nothing from me
But tell me what you think.

ABRAHAM: O Isaac, Isaac, I must thee kill.

ISAAC : Alas, father, is that your will,
Your own child's life here to spill
Upon this hill's brink? . . .

ABRAHAM : O comely creature, unless I thee kill
I offend my God and that sore and ill.
I may not work against his high will
But ever obedient be . . .

ISAAC : Father, since you needs must do so,
Let it pass quickly as it go;
Kneeling here before you low
Your blessing on me spread.

ABRAHAM : My blessing, dear son, give I thee
And thy mother's with heart so free.
The blessing of the Trinity,
My dear son, light on thee.

ISAAC : I pray you, father, cover my eyen,
That I see not your sword so keen;
That stroke must not be seen.
Say no more now to me . . .

ANGEL : Abraham, my servant dear.

ABRAHAM: Lo, Lord, I am already here.

ANGEL : Lay not thy sword in no manner
On Isaac, thy dear darling.

Nay! do him no injury.
For thou dreadest God, well I see
That on thy son thou hast no mercy
To do his bidding ...

ABRAHAM: Ah, Lord of heaven and King of bliss,
Thy bidding I shall do in this.
Sacrifice here to me sent is,
And all, Lord, through thy grace.

A horned wether here I see
Among the briars tied is he.
Offered to thee it shall be
Anon right in this place.

GOD: Abraham, by my self I swear
Thou hast been so obedient e'er
And spared not thy son so dear
To fulfil my bidding.

Thou shall be blessed, thou art worthy,
Thy seed I shall multiply
As the stars and sand, so say I,
Of thy body coming.

And all nations, believe thou me,
Blessed ever more shall be
Through fruit that shall come of thee
And all the good be made glad.

ANONYMOUS

(from the Chester Cycle of Miracle Plays,
translated from the Early English by Maurice Hussey)

eyen: eyes
wether: ram

INTO EGYPT

I

Trading in spices, once they bought a slave;
not something they remembered and retold,
but into Egypt was a longish way.

They must have made sure he would not escape.
Roped to a camel by his wrist or waist,
was he their equal or an animal;
did one abuse him and another say,
he will recover and can still be sold?

II

Bold were the stars like the eyes of his brothers,
far were his dreams like his father's tents;
night herded child and strangers together
as the desert stampeded before the wind.

III

Perhaps they tamed him as they went
with stories of huge monuments,
water as wanton as the sun
and green fur covering the plain
and towns exuberant with men.

IV

Later, they liked him better than their own:
a mascot with sweet pastures in his head;
I see him burning, bird-boned, gently bred,
beguiling twenty brigands with his dreams.
Perhaps they had agreed to take him back
– a motherless boy who made them feel strong –
and outside Egypt told him, stay here, wait;

but he had found his footprints on the track:
his children's children going the other way,
and like a prince bid them, take me along.

KAREN GERSHON

THE BURNING BUSH

When Moses, musing in the desert, found
The thorn bush spiking up from the hot ground,
And saw the branches, on a sudden, bear
The crackling yellow barberries of fire,

He searched his learning and imagination
For any logical, neat explanation,
And turned to go, but turned again and stayed,
And faced the fire and knew it for his God.

I too have seen the briar alight like coal,
The love that burns, the flesh that's ever whole,
And many times have turned and left it there,
Saying: 'It's prophecy – but metaphor.'

But stinging tongues like John the Baptist shout:
'That this is metaphor is no way out.
It's dogma too, or you make God a liar;
The bush is still a bush, and fire is fire.'

NORMAN NICHOLSON

barberries: spiny shrubs with yellow flowers and red berries

THAT NIGHT

I

That night they waited shut inside their houses,
fully dressed and their belongings packed;
small children lay where sleep had caught them up,
older ones watched their parents being afraid.
And then it came: a brief scream far away,
and then another, closer, and another;
a youngest child – my ancestor – exclaimed,
if they don't see the sign they'll kill my brother!

II

Where the angel went that night
the houses became loud and light;
in the slave part of the town
they stayed dark and without sound.

III

I think my mother would have said,
not at the cost of so much blood;
we shall remain the slaves of life,
better the suffering we know ...
and would have been content enough
to weep that it was time to go.

IV

If we had been the children there
– we too went to the school of death –
we would have gone where Moses was,
enticed from our families
by promises that needed us;
we would have been his messengers.

V

In that night slavery passed like a storm;
and still, to raise what had been beaten down
needed a lifetime between dusk and dawn.

KAREN GERSHON

OCCASIONS DREW ME EARLY
TO THIS CITY

A Messenger describes the death of Samson

Occasions drew me early to this City,
And as the gates I enter'd with Sun-rise,
The morning Trumpets Festival proclaim'd
Through each high street: little I had dispatch't
When all abroad was rumour'd that this day
Samson should be brought forth to shew the people
Proof of his mighty strength in feats and games;
I sorrow'd at his captive state, but minded
Not to be absent at that spectacle.
The building was a spacious Theatre
Half round on two main Pillars vaulted high,
With seats where all the Lords and each degree
Of sort, might sit in order to behold,
The other side was op'n, where the throng
On banks and scaffolds under Skie might stand;
I among these aloof obscurely stood.
The Feast and noon grew high, and Sacrifice
Had fill'd thir hearts with mirth, high chear, and wine,
When to their sports they turn'd. Immediately

67

Was *Samson* as a public servant brought,
In thir state Livery clad; before him Pipes
And Timbrels, on each side went armed guards,
Both horse and foot before him and behind
Archers, and Slingers, Cataphracts and Spears.
At sight of him the people with a shout
Rifted the Air clamouring thir god with praise,
Who had made thir dreadful enemy thir thrall.
He patient but undaunted where they led him,
Came to the place, and what was set before him
Which without help of eye, might be assay'd,
To heave, pull, draw, or break, he still perform'd
All with incredible, stupendious force,
None daring to appear Antagonist.
At length for intermission sake they led him
Between the pillars; he his guide requested
(For so from such as nearer stood we heard)
As over-tir'd to let him lean a while
With both his arms on those two massie Pillars
That to the arched roof gave main support.
He unsuspitious led him; which when *Samson*
Felt in his arms, with head a while enclin'd,
And eyes fast fixt he stood, as one who pray'd,
Or some great matter in his mind revolv'd.
At last with head erect thus cryed aloud,
Hitherto, Lords, what your commands impos'd
I have perform'd, as reason was, obeying,
Not without wonder or delight beheld.
Now of my own accord such other tryal
I mean to shew you of my strength, yet greater;
As with amaze shall strike all who behold.
This utter'd, straining all his nerves he bow'd,

As with the force of winds and waters pent,
When Mountains tremble, those two massie Pillars
With horrible convulsion to and fro,
He tugg'd, he shook, till down they came and drew
The whole roof after them, with burst of thunder
Upon the heads of all who sate beneath,
Lords, Ladies, Captains, Councellors, or Priests,
Thir choice nobility and flower, not only
Of this but each *Philistian* City round
Met from all parts to solemnize this Feast.
Samson with these immixt, inevitably
Pull'd down the same destruction on himself;
The vulgar only scap'd who stood without.

JOHN MILTON
(from *Samson Agonistes*)

occasions: personal affairs; matters of business
dispatch't: various commitments dealt with
banks: benches
timbrels: tambourines
cataphracts: soldiers in full armour, on horses also heavily mailed
spears: spearmen
thrall: slave
immixt: mixed up with
vulgar: the common people

GOLIATH AND THE PEBBLE

David looking on Goliath saw
A man so huge he sank into the world
As deep as to his ankles into dust.

Goliath, under eyelids of disdain,
A child shape tiny upon unbent grass,
A shape so small it stood there shadowless.

Yet David in his prayer was the globe
And stood as tall as from the depth of earth,
And rose upon such rock legs high enough

To touch his head to God.
He need not heed the bull-shield thunderer
Nor dread the spear's slim weight in air

As, scooping stone from off its anvil, earth,
He hooked it in a cunning web of hide
Then cast it from a string, his childish sling.

The Giant, who heretofore bestrid the world
To nod at pebbles, found his little world a pebble
And was felled by stones as big as earth in air.

MICHAEL BALDWIN

KING DAVID

King David was a sorrowful man:
   No cause for his sorrow had he:
And he called for the music of a hundred harps,
   To solace his melancholy.

70

They played till they all fell silent:
 Played – and play sweet did they;
But the sorrow that haunted the heart of King David
 They could not charm away.

He rose; and in his garden
 Walked by the moon alone,
A nightingale hidden in a cypress-tree
 Jargoned on and on.

King David lifted his sad eyes
 Into the dark-boughed tree –
'Tell me, thou little bird that singest,
 Who taught my grief to thee?'

But the bird in no wise heeded;
 And the king in the cool of the moon
Hearkened to the nightingale's sorrowfulness,
 Till all his own was gone.

WALTER DE LA MARE

HENCE, DAVID, WALK THE SOLITARY WOODS

Hence, David, walk the solitary woods,
And in some cedar's shade the thunder slew,
And fire from heaven hath made his branches black,
Sit mourning the decease of Absalon:
Against the body of that blasted plant
In thousand shivers break thy ivory lute,
Hanging thy stringless harp upon his boughs;
And through the hollow sapless sounding trunk

71

Bellow the torments that perplex thy soul.
There let the winds sit sighing till they burst;
Let tempest, muffled with a cloud of pitch,
Threaten the forests with her hellish face,
Then let them toss my broken lute to heaven,
Even to his hands that beats me with the strings,
To show how sadly his poor shepherd sings.

GEORGE PEELE
(from *The Love of King David and Queen Bethsabe*)

THE HOOPOE

A rare one with us –
King Solomon's messenger to the Queen of Sheba;
Sheltered that wise king
From the heat of the midday sun.

He offered a reward – they asked
For crowns of gold.

Poor silly birds – soon everybody harried them
With sticks and stones, until the king
Turned the gold crowns to feathers.
A feathered crown is best.

JOHN HEATH-STUBBS

hoopoe: crested bird, native of Africa; one of its species migrates to Europe,
and occasionally to Britain

THE PLOTTING PRINCES
APPROACH THE
KING

The plotting princes approach the king.
'Darius,' they say, 'may your reign be long!
The captains of your court have counselled together
To establish a statute, a stern decree.
This have we thought. For thirty days
Whosoever shall ask a petition
Of any save thee shall be thrown straightway
Alive to the lions. Long live Darius!
Wilt thou sign, great king, and seal the writing,
That none may annul this new law?'
Then Darius, thinking no evil,
Signs and seals it. The sinful men
Hurry hence to the house of Daniel
Where, at a window towards Jerusalem,
The prophet is praying with pure heart
To the true God. They return to Darius.
'O king,' they cry, 'thy decree went forth
That whosoever should ask a petition
Of any save thee should be thrown to the lions,
But this man Daniel has dared disobey thee,
Openly he asks for help from his God.'
Darius is sad, he sees their envy,
He labours long to deliver Daniel.
But the accusers cry: 'The decree was thine,
Didst thou not sign and seal the writing
That none should annul it? It shall not be changed.'
'Alas,' says the king, 'the law is thus.'
Grieving greatly, he gives orders

That Daniel be cast in the den of lions.
'Daniel,' he cries, 'I can do no other.
Forgive thy friend! May God save thee!'

So Daniel is down in the deep pit,
Alone among lions. But the Lord of Heaven
Sends an angel with a sword to keep
Those beasts at bay that they bite him not.
And a second angel He sends in the night
To Habbakuk, a holy prophet,
Saying, 'Arise! The road is long.
I am bid to bring you to Babylon town
And the dark den where Daniel lies.'
'That is full far,' says that faithful man,
'And I know not the way, nevertheless
I will go to greet him.' God's angel
Takes him by the hair, in a trice they come
To the perilous pit, he appears to Daniel,
Refreshes with food his fainting spirit.

Day dawns, to the den of lions
The king is come. He calls aloud,
'Daniel, O Daniel, my dear friend,
Dost thou live yet? Hath the Lord thy God
Saved His servant from sudden death?'
And Daniel answers: 'Hail, O king!
I am safe and sound. God sent an angel
With a shining sword to shut the mouths
Of the hungry lions. They lie asleep.'
Glad is Darius at this great wonder,
Bids his bodyguard bring up Daniel,

Set him free, and in fury commands:
'Let his accusers be cast in the pit!'
The princes and presidents who plotted evil
Rue their wrong. Ere they reach the bottom
Their bones are broken, their bodies rent,
Torn in pieces by the teeth of the lions.
So Daniel was restored to his state of honour
And dwelt in peace until his days' end.
Visions revealed to him events to come,
Truly he foretold the return of Judah
To its own home, and the end of Jerusalem,
Her final fall when, in the fullness of time,
The wise Word that was from the beginning,
Maker of all things, should be made flesh
And suffer death to redeem mankind.

W. H. AUDEN
(from *Daniel: a sermon*)

This free verse adaptation of the Daniel story was written by W. H. Auden to be read aloud by an actor between the scenes of the New York Pro Musica's presentation of the twelfth-century musical drama *The Play of Daniel* when it was performed at The Cloisters, the Metropolitan Museum of Art, New York, in 1958.

JONAH

He stands in rags upon the heaving prow
Stiff as the mast behind him, and the rain
Channels the filthy wrinkles of his brow,
Driving to Nineveh. Beneath his brain
That severs their bruised water like a keel,
Yeasty with spirit, mount the rebel streams
And scatter on his lips their yellow foam.

Then that extreme volition he would flee
Pours downwards its green fury, snaps his bands,
As, final mutiny, the Prophet's hands
Rise up and fling him to the hungry sea.

How gently then the mercy takes this child
Into a silence, turns, and with her choice
Swims through the mild embraces of the flood
To that great city hungry for his voice.

THOMAS BLACKBURN

VOICES
AND
VISIONS

THE TEN COMMANDMENTS

(1731)

I. Have thou no other gods but me,
II. And to no image bow thy knee.
III. Take not the name of God in vain:
IV. The sabbath day do not profane.
V. Honour thy father and mother too;
VI. And see that thou no murder do.
VII. Abstain from words and deeds unclean;
VIII. Nor steal, though thou art poor and mean.
IX. Bear not false witness, shun that blot;
X. What is thy neighbour's covet not.

These laws, O Lord, write in my heart, that I,
May in thy faithful service live and die.

ANONYMOUS

LOVE

Love bade me welcome; yet my soul drew back,
    Guilty of dust and sin.
But quick-eyed Love, observing me grow slack
    From my first entrance in,
Drew nearer to me, sweetly questioning,
    If I lacked anything.

'A guest', I answered, 'worthy to be here.'
    Love said, 'You shall be he.'
'I, the unkind, ungrateful? Ah, my dear,
    I cannot look on thee.'

78

Love took my hand, and smiling did reply,
    'Who made the eyes but I?'

'Truth, Lord, but I have marred them; let my shame
    Go where it doth deserve.'
'And know you not', says Love, 'who bore the blame?'
    'My dear, then I will serve.'
'You must sit down', says Love, 'and taste my meat.'
    So I did sit and eat.

GEORGE HERBERT

A NEW DIAL

In those twelve days let us be glad,
For God of his power hath all things made.

What are they that are but one?
One God, one Baptism, and one Faith,
One Truth there is, the scripture saith:

What are they that are but two?
Two Testaments, the old and new,
We do acknowledge to be true:

What are they that are but three?
Three Persons are in Trinity
Which make one God in unity:

What are they that are but four?
Four sweet Evangelists there are,
Christ's birth, life, death, which do declare:

What are they that are but five?
Five Senses, like five kings, maintain

In every man a several reign:

What are they that are but six?
Six Days to labour is not wrong,
For God himself did work so long:

What are they that are but seven?
Seven Liberal Arts hath God sent down
With divine skill man's soul to crown:

What are they that are but eight?
Eight Beatitudes are there given;
Use them aright and go to heaven:

What are they that are but nine?
Nine Muses, like the heavens' nine spheres,
With sacred tunes entice our ears:

What are they that are but ten?
Ten Statutes God to Moses gave,
Which, kept or broke, do spill or save:

What are they that are but eleven?
Eleven thousand Virgins did partake,
And suffered death for Jesus' sake:

What are they that are but twelve?
Twelve are attending on God's Son;
Twelve make our Creed. The dial's done.

ANONYMOUS

Eleven thousand Virgins: a reference to St Ursula, a fifth (?)-century saint
martyred in Cologne with her companions, ten noble virgins: a number
that seems to have been greatly enlarged as fact merged with legend

I AM THE GREAT SUN

I am the great sun, but you do not see me,
  I am your husband, but you turn away.
I am the captive, but you do not free me,
  I am the captain you will not obey.

I am the truth, but you will not believe me,
  I am the city where you will not stay,
I am your wife, your child, but you will leave me,
  I am that God to whom you will not pray.

I am your counsel, but you do not hear me,
  I am the lover whom you will betray,
I am the victor, but you do not cheer me,
  I am the holy dove whom you will slay.

I am your life, but if you will not name me,
Seal up your soul with tears, and never blame me.

CHARLES CAUSLEY

IN MIDWINTER A WOOD WAS

In midwinter a wood was
where the sand-coloured deer ran
through quietness.
It was a marvellous thing
to see those deer running.

Softer than ashes
snow lay all winter where they ran,
and in the wood a holly tree was.

God, it was a marvellous thing
to see the deer running.

Between lime trunks grey or green
branch-headed stags went by
silently trotting.
A holly tree dark and crimson
sprouted at the wood's centre, thick and high
without a whisper, no other berry so fine.

Outside the wood was black midwinter,
over the downs that reared so solemn
wind rushed in gales, and strong here
wrapped around wood and holly fire
(where deer among the close limes ran)
with a storming circle of its thunder.
Under the trees it was a marvellous thing
to see the deer running.

PETER LEVI

THE FULLNESS OF TIME

On a rusty iron throne
Past the furthest star of space
I saw Satan sit alone,
Old and haggard was his face;
For his work was done and he
Rested in eternity.

And to him from out the sun
Came his father and his friend
Saying, now the work is done

Enmity is at an end:
And he guided Satan to
Paradises that he knew.

Gabriel without a frown,
Uriel without a spear,
Raphael came singing down
Welcoming their ancient peer,
And they seated him beside
One who had been crucified.

JAMES STEPHENS

THE SEVENTH ANGEL

The seventh angel
is completely different
even his name is different
Szemkel

he is not like Gabriel
the golden
pillar of the throne
and baldachin

nor like Raphael
the choir-tuner

nor even
Azrael
engineer of the planets
geometer of infinity
splendid exponent of theoretical physics

Szemkel
is black and nervous
and has been fined many times for
illegal import of sinners

between the abyss
and the heavens
without a rest his feet go pit-a-pit

his sense of dignity is non-existent
and they only keep him in the squad
out of consideration for the number seven

but he is not like the others
not like the hetman of the hosts
Michael
all scales and feathery plumes

nor like Azrafael
interior decorator of the universe
warden of its luxuriant vegetation
his wings shimmering like two oak trees

nor even like
Dedrael
apologist and cabalist

Szemkel Szemkel
... the angels complain
why can't you be splendid?

the Byzantine artists
when they paint all seven
reproduce Szemkel
just like the rest

because they fear
they might lapse into heresy
if they were to portray him
just as he is
black nervous
with his old halo tarnished.

ZBIGNIEW HERBERT
(translated from the Polish by Peter Dale Scott)

The Revelation of St John the Divine (Ch. 8:v.2) speaks of 'the seven
  angels which stood before God'.
baldachin: richly embroidered canopy over an altar or throne
hetman: Polish or Cossack army commander
cabalist: secret schemer or plotter

MICHAEL, ARCHANGEL

Michael, Archangel
Of the King of Kings,
Give ear to our voices.

Thou wert seen in the Temple of God,
A censer of gold in thy hands,
And the smoke of it fragrant with spices
Rose up till it came before God.

Thou with strong hand didst smite the cruel dragon,
And many souls didst rescue from his jaws.
Then was there a great silence in heaven,
And a thousand thousand saying 'Glory to the Lord
    King'.

85

Hear us, Michael,
Greatest angel,
Come down a little
From thy high seat,
To bring us the strength of God
And the lightening of His mercy.

And do thou, Gabriel,
Lay low our foes,
And thou, Raphael,
Heal our sick,
Purge our disease, ease thou our pain,
And give us to share
In the joys of the blessed.

ALCUIN
(translated from the Medieval Latin by Helen Waddell)

THE BARRANONG ANGEL CASE

You see that bench in front of Meagher's store?
That's where the angel landed.
What? An angel?
Yes. It was just near smoko time on a sale day.
Town was quite full. He called us all together.
And was he obeyed?
Oh yes. He got a hearing.
Made his announcement, blessed us and took off
Again, straight up.
He had most glorious wings . . .
What happened then?
There were some tasks he'd set us

86

Or rather that sort of followed from his message.
And were they carried out?
At first we meant to,
But after a while, when there had been some talk
Most came to think he'd been a bit, well, haughty,
A bit overdone, with those flourishes of wings
And that plummy accent.
Lot of the women liked that.
But the men who'd knelt, off their own bat, mind you,
They were specially crook on him, as I remember.

Did he come again?
Oh yes. The message was important.
The second time, he hired the church hall,
Spoke most politely, called us all by name.
Any result?
Not much. At first we liked him.
But, after all, he'd singled out the Catholics.
It was their hall. And another thing resented
By different ones, he hadn't charged admission.
We weren't all paupers, and any man or angel
With so little regard for local pride, or money,
Ends up distrusted.

Did he give up then?
Oh no. The third time round
He thought he had our measure. Came by car,
Took a room at Morgan's, didn't say a word
About his message for the first two days
And after that, dropped hints. Quite clever ones.
He made sure, too, that he spoke to all the Baptists.
I'll bet that worked.
You reckon? Not that I saw.

We didn't like him pandering to our ways
For a start. Some called it mockery, straight out.
He was an angel, after all. And then
There was the way he kept on coming back
Hustling the people.
And when all's said and done
He was a stranger. And he talked religion.

Did he keep on trying?
No. Gave us away.
Would it have helped if he'd settled in the district?
Don't think so, mate. If you follow me, he was
Too keen altogether. He'd have harped on that damn
    message
All the time – or if he'd stopped, well then
He'd have been despised because he'd given in, like.
He'd just got off on the wrong foot from the start
And you can't fix that up.

But what – Oh Hell! – what if he'd been, say, born here?
Well, that sort of thing's a bit above an angel,
Or a bit below. And he'd grow up too well known.
Who'd pay any heed to a neighbour's boy, I ask you,
Specially if he came out with messages?
Besides, what he told us had to do with love
And people here,
They don't think that's quite – manly.

LES A. MURRAY

smoko: a break from work (Australian slang)
crook on: hostile to; abusive

HOSPITAL FOR DEFECTIVES

By your unnumbered charities
A miracle disclose,
Lord of the Images, whose love,
The eyelid and the rose,
Takes for a language, and to-day
Tell to me what is said
By these men in a turnip field
And their unleavened bread.

For all things seem to figure out
The stirrings of your heart,
And two men pick the turnips up
And two men pull the cart;
And yet between the four of them
No word is ever said
Because the yeast was not put in
Which makes the human bread.
But three men stare on vacancy
And one man strokes his knees;
What is the meaning to be found
In such dark vowels as these?

Lord of the Images, whose love,
The eyelid and the rose,
Takes for a metaphor, today
Beneath the warder's blows,
The unleavened man did not cry out
Or turn his face away;
Through such men in a turnip field
What is it that you say?

THOMAS BLACKBURN

89

LOWERY COT

(for Robert Graves)

This is the house where Jesse White
Run staring in one misty night,
And said he seed the Holy Ghost
Out to Lowery finger-post.

Said It rised up like a cloud
Muttering to Itself out loud,
And stood tremendous on the hill
While all the breathing world was still.

They put en shivering to bed,
And in three days the man was dead.
Gert solemn visions such as they
Be overstrong for mortal clay.

L. A. G. STRONG

CHRISTMAS

ST JOSEPH AND GOD'S MOTHER

St Joseph and God's Mother,
  They kept good company,
And they rode out of Nazareth
  So early in the day.

They found no place to rest in,
  No place in all the town,
And there they made an arbour,
  Of reeds and grasses brown.

St Joseph went to look for fire,
  No fire there could he see,
And when he came to Mary,
  The Babe was on her knee,
As white as is the milk,
  As red as rose was He.

St Joseph looked upon Him:
  'O what is this fair thing?
This is no child of mine,
  This comes from heaven's King.'

By there came three shepherds
  To wish Him a good day,
The two upon their fiddles,
  The third his bells did play.

And there they played sweet music,
  All for to make Him mirth;
Three hours have not gone yet
  Since our Saviour's birth.

'Dance, Maiden Mary,
  Dance, Mother mild,

And if you will dance with me,
    The ass will hold the Child.'

'I will not dance, Joseph,
    My husband so dear,
But if you will dance for joy,
    Dance, husband, here.'

Joseph then began to dance
    With all his might and main;
The mother smiled and said to him
    'Joseph is young again.'

'And if I rejoice, Mary,
    Well ought that to be;
Here is born to us to-night
    The King of glory.'

ANONYMOUS
(translated from the Spanish by Edith C. Batho)

MANGERS

Who knows the name and country now,
    Of that rich man who lived of old;
Whose horses fed at silver mangers,
    And drank of wine from troughs of gold?

He who was in a manger born,
    By gold and silver undefiled –
Is known as Christ to every man,
    And Jesus to a little child.

W. H. DAVIES

THE ANGELS FOR THE NATIVITY
OF OUR LORD

Run, shepherds, run where Bethlem blest appears,
We bring the best of news, be not dismayed,
A Saviour there is born more old than years,
Amidst heaven's rolling heights this earth who stayed:
In a poor cottage inned, a virgin maid
A weakling did him bear, who all upbears;
There is he, poorly swaddled, in manger laid,
To whom too narrow swaddlings are our spheres:
Run, shepherds, run, and solemnize his birth,
This is that night – no, day, grown great with bliss,
In which the power of Satan broken is;
In heaven be glory, peace unto the earth!
    Thus singing, through the air the angels swam,
    And cope of stars re-echoèd the same.

WILLIAM DRUMMOND

CHRISTMAS EVE AT SEA

A wind is rustling 'south and soft',
    Cooing a quiet country tune,
The calm sea sighs, and far aloft
    The sails are ghostly in the moon.

Unquiet ripples lisp and purr,
    A block there pipes and chirps i' the sheave,
The wheel-ropes jar, the reef-points stir
    Faintly – and it is Christmas Eve.

The hushed sea seems to hold her breath,
    And o'er the giddy, swaying spars,
Silent and excellent as Death,
    The dim blue skies are bright with stars.

Dear God – they shone in Palestine
    Like this, and yon pale moon serene
Looked down among the lowing kine
    On Mary and the Nazarene.

The angels called from deep to deep,
    The burning heavens felt the thrill,
Startling the flocks of silly sheep,
    And lonely shepherds on the hill.

To-night beneath the dripping bows
    Where flashing bubbles burst and throng,
The bow-wash murmurs and sighs and soughs
    A message from the angels' song.

The moon goes nodding down the west,
    The drowsy helmsman strikes the bell;
Rex Judaeorum natus est,
    I charge you, brothers, sing Nowell, Nowell,
Rex Judaeorum natus est.

JOHN MASEFIELD

sheave: wheel with a grooved rim; pulley of a pulley-block
reef-points: short lengths of rope to secure a sail when reefed
silly: innocent; simple

THE STARRY NIGHT

That starry Night when Christ was born,
The shepherds watched by Dead Man's Thorn;
They shared their supper with the dogs,
And watched the sparks flick from the logs
Where the coppings from the holly burned.

Then the dogs growled, and faces turned
To horsemen, coming from the hill.

A Captain called to them, 'Keep still . . .
We're riding, seeking for a sign
That human beings are divine . . .
Is there such marvel, hereabout?'

The shepherds said, 'Us don't know nowt.
We're Mr Jones's shepherd chaps.
Old Mr Jones might know, perhaps . . .
But if you've come this country road,
You've passed his house and never knowed.
There's someone in the town might know;
A mile on, keeping as you go.'

Long after all had disappeared,
More horsemen (from the woodland), neared;
And one, a King, with a dark skin,
Cried, 'Friends, are gods and men akin?
A wonder tells of this, they say.
Is it near here? Is this the way?'

'Why, no,' the shepherds said . . . 'Perhaps.
We're Mr Jones's shepherd chaps.
Old Mr Jones would know, I wis,

But he'll be gone to bed by this.'

After the troop had passed away,
A third came (from the River way)
And cried, 'Good friends, we seek to find
Some guidance for the questing mind,
Eternity, in all this Death,
Some life out-living flesh and breath.
Can we find this, the way we ride?'

'You'd better picket down and bide,'
The shepherds said, 'And rest your bones.
We're shepherds here to Mr Jones.
When morning comes, you ask of he,
For he'd know more of that than we.
We're only shepherds here; so bide.'

'We cannot wait,' the horseman cried.
'Life cannot wait; Death cannot stay;
This midnight is our only day.
Push on, friends; shepherds all, farewell.
This living without Life is Hell.'

The clatter of the horse-hoofs failed,
Along the wood a barn-owl wailed;
The small mice rustled in the wood;
The stars burned in their multitude.

Meanwhile, within the little town,
The camping horsemen settled down;
The horses drank at stream and fed
On chaff, from nose-bags, picketed.
The men rolled blankets out, and stretched;
Black Nim their hard cheese supper fetched;

Then, after spirit from the gourd,
Each turned to sleep without a word,
But shortly roused again to curse
A some-one calling for a nurse
To help a woman in her woe.

All this was very long ago.

JOHN MASEFIELD

coppings: perhaps from 'coppice', a small wood kept so by periodical cutting
I wis: certainly; surely

THE SHEPHERDS' CAROL

We stood on the hills, Lady,
Our day's work done,
Watching the frosted meadows
That winter had won.

The evening was calm, Lady,
The air so still,
Silence more lovely than music
Folded the hill.

There was a star, Lady,
Shone in the night,
Larger than Venus it was
And bright, so bright.

Oh, a voice from the sky, Lady,
It seemed to us then
Telling of God being born
In the world of men.

And so we have come, Lady,
Our day's work done,
Our love, our hopes, ourselves
We give to your son.

ANONYMOUS

ALL IN TUNE TO WILLIAM'S FLUTE

All in tune to William's flute
Now is Robin's tabor,
Dance to-night and sing high praise
As they did in other days,
Every kindly neighbour.
All in tune, all in tune,
Are the flute and tambourine,
All in tune, all in tune,
Heaven and earth to-night are seen.

God and man are in accord,
More than flute or tabor,
Dance for joy and sing with awe,
For the child upon the straw
Is our God and neighbour.
God and man, God and man,
Are like flute and tambourine,
God and man, God and man,
As true neighbours here are seen.

ANONYMOUS

A COUNTRY CAROL

Deep in the woods the foxes bark,
And skinned of cloud the moon rides high.
In meadows where the summer lark
Untwists her song, snow-banks lie.
    The faithful say
    This winter night is articled,
    Auspicious for the burning child.

A country coming is foretold
As usual. Stall, ox, and ass
Are ready. Someone has lit the lamps and boiled
Water. Straw bales gleam like brass.
    The faithful pray
    Let God and man be reconciled,
    And keep the bargain of the burning child.

Their prayers swarm up as glib as mottoes,
Leaving behind them other members of the feast:
Broilers penned in twilight ghettos,
Shackled calves, and rabbits dying of pest.
    The burning child descends,
    A mirror for our charity.
    This time, for us to burn; for us to die.

PHILIP OAKES

THE BURNING BABE

As I in hoary winter's night
   Stood shivering in the snow,
Surprised I was with sudden heat
   Which made my heart to glow;
And lifting up a fearful eye
   To view what fire was near,
A pretty Babe all burning bright
   Did in the air appear;
Who, scorchèd with excessive heat,
   Such floods of tears did shed,
As though His floods should quench His flames,
   Which with His tears were fed.
'Alas!' quoth He, 'but newly born
   In fiery heats I fry,
Yet none approach to warm their hearts
   Or feel my fire but I!

'My faultless breast the furnace is;
   The fuel, wounding thorns;
Love is the fire, and sighs the smoke;
   The ashes, shames and scorns;
The fuel Justice layeth on,
   And Mercy blows the coals,
The metal in this furnace wrought
   Are men's defilèd souls:
For which, as now on fire I am
   To work them to their good,
So will I melt into a bath,
   To wash them in my blood.'

With this He vanish'd out of sight
And swiftly shrunk away,
And straight I callèd unto mind
That it was Christmas Day.

ROBERT SOUTHWELL

THE ANIMALS' CAROL

Christus natus est! the cock Carols on the morning dark.	Christ is born
Quando? croaks the raven stiff Freezing on the broken cliff.	When?
Hoc nocte, replies the crow Beating high above the snow.	This night
Ubi? ubi? booms the ox From its cavern in the rocks.	Where?
Bethlehem, then bleats the sheep Huddled on the winter steep.	Bethlehem
Quomodo? the brown hare clicks, Chattering among the sticks.	How?
Humiliter, the careful wren Thrills upon the cold hedge-stone.	Humbly
Cur? cur? sounds the coot By the iron river-root.	Why?
Propter homines, the thrush Sings on the sharp holly-bush.	For the sake of man

Cui? cui? rings the chough   To whom?
On the strong, sea-haunted bluff.

Mary! Mary! calls the lamb   Mary
From the quiet of the womb.

Praeterea ex quo? cries   Who else?
The woodpecker to pallid skies.

Joseph, breathes the heavy shire   Joseph
Warming in its own blood-fire.

Ultime ex quo? the owl   Who above all?
Solemnly begins to call.

De Deo, the little stare   Of God
Whistles on the hardening air.

Pridem? pridem? the jack snipe   Long ago?
From the harsh grass starts to pipe

Sic et non, answers the fox   Yes and no
Tiptoeing the bitter lough.

Quomodo hoc scire potest?   How do I know this?
Boldly flutes the robin redbreast.

Illo in eandem, squeaks   By going there
The mouse within the barley-sack.

Quae sarcinae? asks the daw   What luggage?
Swaggering from head to claw.

Nulla res, replies the ass,   None
Bearing on its back the Cross.

Quantum pecuniae? shrills   How much money?
The wandering gull about the hills.

Ne nummum quidem, the rook   Not a penny
Caws across the rigid brook.

Nulla resne? barks the dog   Nothing at all?
By the crumbling fire-log.

Nil nisi cor amans, the dove   Only a loving heart
Murmurs from its house of love.

Gloria in Excelsis! Then
Man is God, and God is Man.

CHARLES CAUSLEY

SONG FOR A WINTER BIRTH

Under the watchful lights
    A child was born;
From a mortal house of flesh
    Painfully torn.

And we, who later assembled
    To praise or peer,
Saw merely an infant boy
    Soft sleeping there;

Till he awoke and stretched
    Small arms wide
And, for food or comfort,
    Quavering cried,

A cry and attitude
    Rehearsing, in small,

The deathless death still haunting
    The Place of the Skull.

Outside, in the festive air,
    We lit cigars;
The night was nailed to the sky
    With hard bright stars.

VERNON SCANNELL

TO A YOUNG WRETCH

As gay for you to take your father's axe
As take his gun – rod – to go hunting – fishing.
You nick my spruce until its fibre cracks,
It gives up standing straight and goes down swishing.
You link an arm in its arm and you lean
Across the light snow homeward smelling green.

I could have bought you just as good a tree
To frizzle resin in a candle flame,
And what a saving 'twould have meant to me.
But tree by charity is not the same
As tree by enterprise and expedition.
I must not spoil your Christmas with contrition.

It is your Christmasses against my woods.
But even where thus opposing interests kill,
They are to be thought of as opposing goods
Oftener than as conflicting good and ill;
Which makes the war god seem no special dunce
For always fighting on both sides at once.

And though in tinsel chain and popcorn rope,
My tree a captive in your window bay
Has lost its footing on my mountain slope
And lost the stars of heaven, may, oh, may
The symbol star it lifts against your ceiling
Help me accept its fate with Christmas feeling.

ROBERT FROST

LOST CHRISTMAS

He is alone, it is Christmas.
Up the hill go three trees, the three kings.
There is a star also
Over the dark manger. But where is the Child?

Pity him. He has come far
Like the trees, matching their patience
With his. But the mind was before
Him on the long road. The manger is empty.

R. S. THOMAS

TO EPIPHANY
AND AFTER

NEW YEAR SONG

Now there comes
  The Christmas rose
    But that is eerie
          too like a ghost
    Too like a creature
          preserved under glass
    A blind white fish
          from an underground lake
    Too like last year's widow
        at a window
          And the worst cold's to come.

Now there comes
  The tight-vest lamb
    With its wriggle eel tail
        and its wintry eye
    With its ice-age mammoth
        unconcern
    Letting the aeon
        seconds go by
    With its little peg hooves
        to dot the snow
    Following its mother
        into worse cold and worse
          And the worst cold's to come.

Now there come
  The weak-neck snowdrops
    Bouncing like fountains
        and they stop you, they make you

Take a deep breath
              make your heart shake you
Such a too much of a gift
              for such a mean time
Nobody knows
              how to accept them
All you can do
              is gaze at them baffled
                   And the worst cold's to come.

And now there comes
   The brittle crocus
      To be nibbled by the starving hares
              to be broken by snow
      Now comes the aconite
              purpled by cold
      A song comes into
              the storm-cock's fancy
      And the robin and the wren
              they rejoice like each other
      In an hour of sunlight
              for something important
                   Though the worst cold's to come.

                                        TED HUGHES

MY FATHER PLAYED THE MELODEON

My father played the melodeon
Outside at our gate;
There were stars in the morning east
And they danced to his music.

Across the wild bogs his melodeon called
To Lennons and Callans.
As I pulled on my trousers in a hurry
I knew some strange thing had happened.

Outside in the cow-house my mother
Made the music of milking;
The light of her stable-lamp was a star
And the frost of Bethlehem made it twinkle.

A water-hen screeched in the bog,
Mass-going feet
Crunched the wafer-ice on the pot-holes,
Somebody wistfully twisted the bellows wheel.

My child poet picked out the letters
On the grey stone,
In silver the wonder of a Christmas townland,
The winking glitter of a frosty dawn.

Cassiopeia was over
Cassidy's hanging hill,
I looked and three whin bushes rode across
The horizon – the Three Wise Kings.

An old man passing said:
'Can't he make it talk' –

The melodeon. I hid in the doorway
And tightened the belt of my box-pleated coat.

I nicked six nicks on the door-post
With my penknife's big blade –
There was a little one for cutting tobacco.
And I was six Christmasses of age.

My father played the melodeon,
My mother milked the cows,
And I had a prayer like a white rose pinned
On the Virgin Mary's blouse.

PATRICK KAVANAGH
(from *A Christmas Childhood*)

whin: furze or gorse

III

THE MAGI

Now as at all times I can see in the mind's eye,
In their stiff, painted clothes, the pale unsatisfied ones
Appear and disappear in the blue depth of the sky
With all their ancient faces like rain-beaten stones,
And all their helms of silver hovering side by side,
And all their eyes still fixed, hoping to find once more,
Being by Calvary's turbulence unsatisfied,
The uncontrollable mystery on the bestial floor.

W. B. YEATS

INNOCENT'S SONG

Who's that knocking on the window,
Who's that standing at the door,
What are all those presents
Lying on the kitchen floor?

Who is the smiling stranger
With hair as white as gin,
What is he doing with the children
And who could have let him in?

Why has he rubies on his fingers,
A cold, cold crown on his head,
Why, when he caws his carol,
Does the salty snow run red?

Why does he ferry my fireside
As a spider on a thread,

His fingers made of fuses
And his tongue of gingerbread?

Why does the world before him
Melt in a million suns,
Why do his yellow, yearning eyes
Burn like saffron buns?

Watch where he comes walking
Out of the Christmas flame,
Dancing, double-talking:

Herod is his name.

CHARLES CAUSLEY

THE MIRACULOUS HARVEST

'Rise up, rise up, you merry men all,
    See that you ready be:
All children under two years old
    Now slain they all shall be.'

Then Jesus, aye, and Joseph,
    And Mary that was unknown,
They travelled by a husbandman,
    Just while his seed was sown.

'God speed your work,' said Jesus,
    'Throw all your seed away,
And carry home as ripened corn
    What you have sown this day;

'For to keep your wife and family
    From sorrow, grief, and pain,
And keep Christ in remembrance
    Till seed-time comes again.'

The husbandman fell on his knees,
    Even upon his face;
'Long time hast thou been lookèd for,
    But now thou'rt come at last.

'And I myself do now believe
    Thy name is Jesus called;
Redeemer of mankind thou art,
    Though undeserving all.'

After that there came King Herod,
    With his train so furiously,
Enquiring of the husbandman
    Whether Jesus had passed by.

'Why, the truth it must be spoke,
    And the truth it must be known,
For Jesus he passed by this way,
    Just as my seed was sown.

'But now I have it reapen,
    And some laid in my wain,
Ready to fetch and carry
    Into my barn again.'

'Turn back,' then says the Captain,
    'Your labour and mine's in vain;
It's full three quarters of a year
    Since he his seed has sown.'

So Herod was deceivèd
By the work of God's own hand:
No further he proceeded
Into the Holy Land.

There's thousands of children young,
Which for his sake did die;
Do not forbid those little ones,
And do not them deny.

ANONYMOUS

Another version of this ballad goes under the title of 'The Carnal (the crow) and the Crane'. Many of the legendary stories upon which such ballads are based are found in *The Apocryphal New Testament*.

JOSEPH AND JESUS

Said Joseph unto Mary,
'Be counselled by me:
Fetch your love child from the manger,
For to Egypt we must flee.'

As Mary went a-riding
Up the hill out of view,
The ass was much astonishèd
How like a dove he flew.

Said Jesus unto Joseph,
Who his soft cheek did kiss:

'There are thorns in your beard, good sir.
 I askèd not for this.'

Then Joseph brought to Jesus
 Hot paps of white bread
Which, when it burned that pretty mouth,
 Joseph swallowed in his stead.

ROBERT GRAVES
(from the Spanish)

THE CHILDHOOD OF CHRIST

AS MARY WAS A-WALKING

As Mary was a-walking
    By Bethlehem one day,
Her Son was in her arms,
    So heavenly to see.

'O give me water, Mother.'
    'You cannot drink, my dear;
For the rivers they are muddy,
    And the streams they are not clear;

'The rivers they are muddy,
    And the streams they are not clear,
And the springs are full of blood,
    You cannot drink from here.'

They came into a grove,
    So thick with oranges
That not another orange
    Could hang upon the trees;
There sat a man to guard them,
    Was blind in both his eyes.

'Give me an orange, blind man,
    To feed my Son to-day.'
'And take as many, lady,
    As you can bear away;

'Gather the biggest, lady,
    That most are to your mind,
The small ones soon will ripen,
    If you leave them behind.'

They gathered them by one and one,
    There grew a hundred more,
And straight the man began to see
    That had been blind before.

'O who is this fair lady,
    Has made me see again?'
It was the Holy Virgin
    That walked by Bethlehem.

ANONYMOUS
(translated from the Spanish by Edith C. Batho)

THE BIRDS

When Jesus Christ was four years old,
The angels brought Him toys of gold,
Which no man ever had bought or sold.

And yet with these He would not play.
He made Him small fowl out of clay,
And blessed them till they flew away:
    Tu creasti Domine.

Jesus Christ, Thou child so wise,
Bless mine hands and fill mine eyes,
And bring my soul to Paradise.

                          HILAIRE BELLOC

Tu creasti Domine: Thou hast made all things, O Lord

THE BITTER WITHY

As it fell out on a Holy Day,
   The drops of rain did fall, did fall,
Our Saviour asked leave of His mother Mary
   If He might go play at ball.

'To play at ball, my own dear Son,
   It's time You was going or gone,
But be sure let me hear no complaint of You,
   At night when You do come home.'

It was upling scorn and downling scorn,
   Oh, there He met three jolly jerdins;
Oh, there He asked the jolly jerdins
   If they would go play at ball.

'Oh, we are lords' and ladies' sons,
   Born in bower or in hall,
And You are some poor maid's child
   Born'd in an ox's stall.'

'If you are lords' and ladies' sons,
   Born'd in bower or in hall,
Then at the last I'll make it appear
   That I am above you all.'

Our Saviour built a bridge with the beams of the sun,
   And over it He gone, He gone He.
And after followed the three jolly jerdins,
   And drownded they were all three.

It was upling scorn and downling scorn,
   The mothers of them did whoop and call,

Crying out, 'Mary mild, call home your Child,
  For ours are drownded all.'

Mary mild, Mary mild, called home her Child,
  And laid our Saviour across her knee,
And with a whole handful of bitter withy
  She gave him slashes three.

Then He says to His mother, 'Oh! the withy, oh! the
    withy,
  The bitter withy that causes me to smart, to smart,
Oh! the withy, it shall be the very first tree
  That perishes at the heart.'

ANONYMOUS

withy: tough, flexible branch of willow or osier, used for tying or binding
  bundles
jerdins: children
upling scorn and downling scorn: perhaps, 'up with his ball and down with
  his ball'

THE HOLY WELL

As it fell out one May morning,
  And upon a bright holiday,
Sweet Jesus asked of his dear mother
  If he might go to play.
'To play, to play, sweet Jesus shall go,
  And to play now get you gone;
And let me hear of no complaint
  At night when you come home.'

Sweet Jesus went down to yonder town,
    As far as the Holy Well,
And there did see as fine childrèn
    As any tongue can tell.
He said, 'God bless you every one,
    And your bodies Christ save and see!
And now, little children, I'll play with you,
    And you shall play with me.'

But they made answer to him, 'No!
    Thou art meaner than us all;
Thou art but a simple fair maid's child,
    Born in an ox's stall.'
Sweet Jesus turned him round about,
    Neither laughed, nor smiled, nor spoke;
But the tears came trickling from his eyes
    Like waters from the rock.

Sweet Jesus turned him round about,
    To his mother's dear home went he,
And said, 'I have been in yonder town,
    As after you may see:
I have been down in yonder town,
    As far as the Holy Well;
There did I meet with as fine childrèn
    As any tongue can tell.

'I said, "God bless you every one,
    And your bodies Christ save and see!
And now, little children, I'll play with you,
    And you shall play with me."
But they made answer to me "No";
    They were lords' and ladies' sons,

And I the meanest of them all,
  Born in an ox's stall.'

'Though you are but a maiden's child,
  Born in an ox's stall,
Thou art the Christ, the King of Heaven,
  And the Saviour of them all!
Sweet Jesus, go down to yonder town,
  As far as the Holy Well,
And take away those sinful souls,
  And dip them deep in hell.'

'Nay, nay,' sweet Jesus smiled and said;
  'Nay, nay, that may not be,
For there are too many sinful souls
  Crying out for the help of me.'
Then up spoke the angel Gabriel,
  Upon a good set steven,
'Although you are but a maiden's child,
  You are the King of Heaven!'

ANONYMOUS
(16th century)

meaner: opposite of 'noble'; of low degree
upon a good set steven: in a firm, strong voice

TO EASTER
AND BEYOND

A CHILD'S CALENDAR

No visitors in January.
A snowman smokes a cold pipe in the yard.

They stand about like ancient women,
The February hills.
They have seen many a coming and going, the hills.

In March, Moorfea is littered
With knock-kneed lambs.

Daffodils at the door in April,
Three shawled Marys.
A lark splurges in galilees of sky.

And in May
A russet stallion shoulders the hill apart.
The mares tremble.

The June bee
Bumps in the pane with a heavy bag of plunder.

Strangers swarm in July
With cameras, binoculars, bird books.

He thumped the crag in August,
A blind blue whale.

September crofts get wrecked in blond surges.
They struggle, the harvesters.
They drag loaf and ale-kirn into winter.

In October the fishmonger
Argues, pleads, threatens at the shore.

Nothing in November
But tinkers at the door, keening, with cans.

Some December midnight
Christ, lord, lie warm in our byre.
Here are stars, an ox, poverty enough.

GEORGE MACKAY BROWN

ale-kirn: churn or container of ale, as used at a harvest-supper

ALL IN THE MORNING

It was on Christmas Day,
And all in the morning,
Our Saviour was born,
And our heav'nly King:
    And was not this a joyful thing?
    And sweet Jesus they called him by name.

It was on New Year's Day,
And all in the morning,
They circumcised our Saviour
And our heav'nly King:
    And was not this a joyful thing?
    And sweet Jesus they called him by name.

It was on the Twelfth Day,
And all in the morning,
The wise men were led
To our heav'nly King:
    And was not this a joyful thing?
    And sweet Jesus they called him by name.

It was on Twentieth Day,
And all in the morning,
The wise men returned

From our heav'nly King:
  And was not this a joyful thing?
  And sweet Jesus they called him by name.

It was on Candlemas Day,
And all in the morning,
They visited the Temple
With our heav'nly King:
  And was not this a joyful thing?
  And sweet Jesus they called him by name.

It was on Holy Wednesday,
And all in the morning,
That Judas betrayed
Our dear heav'nly King:
  And was not this a woeful thing?
  And sweet Jesus we'll call him by name.

It was on Sheer Thursday,
And all in the morning,
They plaited a crown of thorns,
For our heav'nly King:
  And was not this a woeful thing?
  And sweet Jesus we'll call him by name.

It was on Good Friday,
And all in the morning,
They crucified our Saviour,
And our heav'nly King:
  And was not this a woeful thing?
  And sweet Jesus we'll call him by name.

It was on Easter Day,
And all in the morning,

Our Saviour arose,
Our own heav'nly King:
The sun and the moon
They did both rise with him,
And sweet Jesus we'll call him by name.

ANONYMOUS

Sheer Thursday: on Maundy Thursday, the Thursday of Holy Week, it
was customary in early times for people to cut their hair and trim
their beards in order that they might be 'honest' (neat and tidy) for
Easter Day

CANDLEMAS EVE

Down with the rosemary and bays,
Down with the mistletoe;
Instead of holly, now up-raise
The greener box, for show.

The holly hitherto did sway:
Let box now domineer
Until the dancing Easter Day,
Or Easter's Eve appear.

Then youthful box, which now hath grace
Your houses to renew,
Grown old, surrender must his place
Unto the crispèd yew.

When yew is out, then birch comes in,
And many flowers beside,
Both of a fresh and fragrant kin,
To honour Whitsun-tide.

Green rushes then, and sweetest bents,
With cooler oaken boughs,
Come in for comely ornaments,
To re-adorn the house.

Thus times do shift, thus times do shift;
Each thing his turn does hold;
New things succeed, new things succeed,
As former things grow old.

ROBERT HERRICK

bents: grass-like reeds or sedges

MOTHERING SUNDAY

It is the day of all the year,
Of all the year the one day,
When I shall see my mother dear
And bring her cheer,
A-mothering on Sunday.

So I'll put on my Sunday coat,
And in my hat a feather,
And get the lines I writ by rote,
With many a note,
That I've a-strung together.

And now to fetch my wheaten cake,
To fetch it from the baker,
He promised me, for mother's sake,
The best he'd bake
For me to fetch and take her.

Well have I known, as I went by
One hollow lane, that none day
I'd fail to find – for all they're shy –
Where violets lie,
As I went home on Sunday.

My sister Jane is waiting-maid
Along with Squire's lady;
And year by year her part she's played,
And home she stayed,
To get the dinner ready.

For mother'll come to church, you'll see –
Of all the year it's the day –
'The one,' she'll say, 'that's made for me.'
And so it be:
It's every mother's free day.

The boys will all come home from town,
Not one will miss that one day;
And every maid will bustle down
To show her gown,
A-mothering on Sunday.

It is the day of all the year,
Of all the year the one day;
And here come I, my mother dear,
To bring you cheer,
A-mothering on Sunday.

GEORGE HARE LEONARD

wheaten cake: the custom is now to bake a simnel cake

THE DONKEY

When fishes flew and forests walked
　　And figs grew upon thorn,
Some moment when the moon was blood
　　Then surely I was born.

With monstrous head and sickening cry
　　And ears like errant wings,
The devil's walking parody
　　On all four-footed things.

The tattered outlaw of the earth,
　　Of ancient crooked will;
Starve, scourge, deride me: I am dumb,
　　I keep my secret still.

Fools! For I also had my hour;
　　One far fierce hour and sweet:
There was a shout about my ears,
　　And palms before my feet.

G. K. CHESTERTON

BALLAD OF THE BREAD MAN

Mary stood in the kitchen
　　Baking a loaf of bread.
An angel flew in through the window.
　　'We've a job for you,' he said.

'God in his big gold heaven,
　　Sitting in his big blue chair,

Wanted a mother for his little son.
  Suddenly saw you there.'

Mary shook and trembled,
  'It isn't true what you say.'
'Don't say that,' said the angel.
  'The baby's on its way.'

Joseph was in the workshop
  Planing a piece of wood.
'The old man's past it,' the neighbours said.
  'That girl's been up to no good.'

'And who was that elegant fellow,'
  They said, 'in the shiny gear?'
The things they said about Gabriel
  Were hardly fit to hear.

Mary never answered,
  Mary never replied.
She kept the information,
  Like the baby, safe inside.

It was election winter.
  They went to vote in town.
When Mary found her time had come
  The hotels let her down.

The baby was born in an annexe
  Next to the local pub.
At midnight, a delegation
  Turned up from the Farmers' Club.

They talked about an explosion
  That made a hole in the sky,

Said they'd been sent to the Lamb & Flag
　To see God come down from on high.

A few days later a bishop
　And a five-star general were seen
With the head of an African country
　In a bullet-proof limousine.

'We've come,' they said, 'with tokens
　For the little boy to choose.'
Told the tale about war and peace
　In the television news.

After them came the soldiers
　With rifle and bomb and gun,
Looking for enemies of the state.
　The family had packed and gone.

When they got back to the village
　The neighbours said, to a man,
'That boy will never be one of us,
　Though he does what he blessed well can.'

He went round to all the people
　A paper crown on his head.
Here is some bread from my father.
　Take, eat, he said.

Nobody seemed very hungry.
　Nobody seemed to care.
Nobody saw the god in himself
　Quietly standing there.

He finished up in the papers.
　He came to a very bad end.

He was charged with bringing the living to life.
   No man was that prisoner's friend.

There's only one kind of punishment
   To fit that kind of a crime.
They rigged a trial and shot him dead.
   They were only just in time.

They lifted the young man by the leg,
   They lifted him by the arm,
They locked him in a cathedral
   In case he came to harm.

They stored him safe as water
   Under seven rocks.
One Sunday morning he burst out
   Like a jack-in-the-box.

Through the town he went walking.
   He showed them the holes in his head.
Now do you want any loaves? he cried.
   'Not today,' they said.

CHARLES CAUSLEY

Lamb & Flag: this well-known inn-sign, showing a lamb holding a banner
  decorated with a cross, has its origins in that part of the Mass beginning
  'Agnus Dei' ('Lamb of God'); an Agnus Dei was a wax tablet stamped
  with such an image, made from what remained of the Easter candles

THE SONG OF THE HOURS

In the first hour of the day
Jesus meek and mild
Was to heathen Pilate led
Like a murderer wild.

He did find Him without sin,
Not condemned to die,
Sent Him therefore from him hence
Unto Herod nigh.

In the third hour of the day
He was scourged and torn
And upon His head was laid
The sharp crown of thorn.

Clad in robes of mock and scorn
He was sore downcast.
And the Cross He had to bear
To His death at last.

In the sixth hour of the day
Nailed upon the Cross
Naked He His Blood outpoured
To our woe and loss.

Those around did scoff at Him
And scoffed the thieves beside,
Till the sun his golden beams
From the sight did hide.

At the ninth hour of the day
Jesus cried: 'O, Father,

Why hast thou forsaken me? ...'
Gall His lips did gather.

Then did He give up the ghost
And the earth did tremble.
The veil of the temple rent,
Mountains they did tumble.

In the last hour of the day
Soldier with his spear
Our Lord Jesus' side did pierce,
Him we love so dear.

Therefrom the red blood and
The water clear did run.
Lo! thus did they crucify
Him of Man the Son!

ANONYMOUS

(translated from the German by James Kirkup)

THE MERCHANTS' CAROL

As we rode down the steep hill-side,
Twelve merchants with our fairing,
A shout across the hollow land
Came loud upon our hearing,
A shout, a song, a thousand strong,
A thousand lusty voices:
'Make haste,' said I,
I knew not why,
'Jerusalem rejoices!'

Beneath the olives fast we rode,
And louder came the shouting:
'So great a noise must mean,' said we,
'A king, beyond all doubting!'
Spurred on, did we, this king to see,
And left the mules to follow;
And nearer, clearer rang the noise
Along the Kidron hollow.

Behold, a many-coloured crowd
About the gate we found there;
But one among them all, we marked,
One man who made no sound there;
Still louder ever rose the crowd's
'Hosanna in the highest!'
'O King,' thought I, 'I know not why
In all this joy thou sighest.'

A Merchant:
'Then he looked up, he looked at me;
But whether he spoke I doubted:
How could I hear so calm a speech
While all the rabble shouted?
And yet these words, it seems, I heard:
"I shall be crowned tomorrow."
They struck my heart with sudden smart,
And filled my bones with sorrow.'

We followed far, we traded not,
But long we could not find him.
The very folk that called him king
Let robbers go and bind him.
We found him then, the sport of men,

Still calm among their crying;
And well we knew his words were true –
He was most kingly dying.

FRANK KENDON

STATIONS OF THE CROSS

(for a chapel in the fields)

Pilate
Our winter jar of grain and malt
Is a Lenten urn.

Cross
Lord, it is time. Take our yoke
And sunwards turn.

First Fall
To drudge in furrows till you drop
Is to be born

Mother of God
Out of that mild mothering hill
And that chaste burn.

Simon
God-begun, the barley-rack
By man is borne.

Veronica
Foldings of women. Your harrow sweat
Darkens her yarn.

Second Fall
Sower-and-seed, one flesh, you stumble
On stone and thorn.

Women of Jerusalem
You are bound for the kingdom of death. The enfolded
Women mourn.

Third Fall
Scythes are sharpened to bring you down,
King Barleycorn.

Stripping
The flails creak. Golden coat
From kernel is torn.

Crucifixion
The fruitful stones thunder around,
Quern on quern.

Death
The last black hunger rages through you
With hoof and horn.

Pietà
Mother, fold him from those furrows,
Your rapt bairn.

Sepulchre
Angel, shepherd, king are kneeling, look,
In the door of the barn.

GEORGE MACKAY BROWN

CROWN OF THORNS

In through the squared window
Blackening from the snow,
Bed, used to death, the old
Man, his wrecked leg stretched out,
Draws and draws. Pencil stub
And paper crumpled like
A brain. The crown of thorns
Draws around the heart. That,
He says, is where it is.

RONALD TAMPLIN

THE WOOD FIRE
(*A Fragment*)

'This is a brightsome blaze you've lit, good friend,
    to-night!'
'– Aye, it has been the bleakest spring I have felt for years,
And nought compares with cloven logs to keep alight:
I buy them bargain-cheap of the executioners,
As I dwell near; and they wanted the crosses out of sight
By Passover, not to affront the eyes of visitors.

'Yes, they're from the crucifixions last week-ending
At Kranion. We can sometimes use the poles again,
But they get split by the nails, and 'tis quicker work than
    mending
To knock together new; though the uprights now and
    then

141

Serve twice when they're let stand. But if a feast's
    impending,
As lately, you've to tidy up for the comers' ken.

'Though only three were impaled, you may know it
    didn't pass off
So quietly as was wont? That Galilee carpenter's son
Who boasted he was king, incensed the rabble to scoff:
I heard the noise from my garden. This piece is the one
    he was on . . .
Yes, it blazes up well if lit with a few dry chips and
    shroff;
And it's worthless for much else, what with cuts and
    stains thereon.'

THOMAS HARDY

shroff: rubbish and light wood used for burning

THE WINDS

There is a tree grows upside down,
    Its roots are in the sky;
Its lower branches reach the earth
    When amorous winds are nigh.

On one lone bough there starkly hangs
    A Man just crucified,
And all the other branches bear
    The choice fruits of the Bride.

When Pleasure's wind goes frisking past,
    Unhallowed by a prayer,

142

It swirls dead leaves from earth-born trees,
    Old growths of pride and care.

The gracious fruits are hidden by
    These leaves of human stain;
The Crucified beneath His load
    Shudders, as if in pain.

But swift springs down a credal wind,
    It thrills through all the boughs;
The dead leaves scatter and are lost;
    The Christ renews His vows.

His hands direct the Spirit's wind
    Branch after branch to shake;
The Bride's fruit drops, and at the touch
    Elected hearts awake.

JACK CLEMO

THE SEVEN VIRGINS

All under the leaves, the leaves of life,
    I met with virgins seven,
And one of them was Mary mild,
    Our Lord's Mother of Heaven.

'O what are you seeking, you seven fair maids,
    All under the leaves of life?
Come tell, come tell me what seek you
    All under the leaves of life.'

'We're seeking for no leaves, Thomas,
    But for a friend of thine;

We're seeking for sweet Jesus Christ,
    To be our guide and thine.'

'Go down, go down to yonder town,
    And sit in the gallery;
And there you'll see sweet Jesus Christ
    Nail'd to a big yew-tree.'

So down they went to yonder town,
    As fast as foot could fall,
And many a grievous bitter tear,
    From the virgins' eyes did fall.

'O peace, Mother, O peace, Mother,
    Your weeping doth me grieve;
O I must suffer this,' He said,
    'For Adam and for Eve.'

'O how can I my weeping leave,
    Or my sorrows undergo,
Whilst I do see my own Son die,
    When sons I have no mo?'

'Dear Mother, dear Mother, you must take John,
    All for to be your son,
And he will comfort you sometimes,
    Mother, as I have done.'

'O, come, thou John Evangelist,
    Thou'rt welcome unto me,
But more welcome my own dear Son,
    That I nursed upon my knee.'

Then He laid his head on His right shoulder,
    Seeing death it struck Him nigh,

144

'The Holy Ghost be with your soul, –
I die, Mother dear, I die.'

O the rose, the rose, the gentle rose,
 And the fennel that grows so green!
God give us grace in every place,
 To pray for our king and queen.

Furthermore for our enemies all
 Our prayers they should be strong.
Amen, Good Lord! Your charity
 Is the ending of my song.

ANONYMOUS
(16th century)

'O, MY HEART IS WOE!'

'O, my heart is woe!' Mary she said so,
'For to see my dear son die, and sons I have no mo.'

'When that my sweet son was thirty winter old,
Then the traitor Judas waxèd very bold:
For thirty plates of money his master he had sold.
But when I it wistè, Lord, my heart was cold!

'Upon Sherè Thursday then truly it was
On my sonnès death that Judas did compàss.
Many were the false Jews that followed him by trace;
And there before them all he kissed my sonnès face.

'My son before Pilate brought was he,
And Peter said three times he knew him not, pardee.

145

Pilate said unto the Jews: "What say ye?"
Then they cried with one voice: *"Crucifige!"*

'On Good Friday, at the mount of Calvary,
My son was done on the cross, nailed with nailès three.
Of all the friends that he had, never one could he see
But gentle John the Evangelist, that still stood him by.

'Though I were sorrowful, no man have at it wonder;
For huge was the earthquake, horrible was the thunder.
I looked on my sweet son on the cross that I stood under;
Then came Longeus with a spear and cleft his heart in
   sunder.'

ANONYMOUS

plates: pieces
wistè: knew
compàss: contrive; plan
Longeus: also known as Longius or Longinus, the traditional name of
   the Roman soldier who struck Christ's side with a spear at the Crucifixion

MARY'S WANDERING

Once Mary would go wandering,
To all the lands would run,
That she might find her son.

Whom met she as she journeyed forth?
Saint Peter, that good man,
Who sadly did her scan.

'O tell me have you seen him yet –
The one I love the most –
The son whom I have lost?'

146

'Too well, too well, I've seen thy son;
'Twas by a palace-gate,
Most grievous was his state.'

'O say, what wore he on his head?'
'A crown of thorns he wore;
A cross he also bore.'

'Ah me! and he must bear that cross,
Till he's brought to the hill,
For cruel men to kill.'

'Nay, Mary, cease thy weeping, dear:
The wounds they are but small;
But heaven is won for all!'

*Most grievous was his state
But heaven is won for all.*

ANONYMOUS
(translated from the German)

CHRIST HARROWS HELL

Hold still
Truth said: I hear some spirit
Speaking to the guards of hell,
And see him too, telling them
Unbar the gates. 'Lift your heads
You gates'
And from the heart
Of light
A loud voice spoke.
Open
These gates, Lucifer,
Prince of this land: the King of glory,
A crown upon his head
Comes.

Satan groaned and said to his hell's angels,
'It's that sort of light sprung Lazarus.
Unstoppable. This'll be big, big
Trouble, I mean all sorts of bother
For the lot of us. If this bigshot
Gets in he'll fetch the lot out, take them
Wherever that Lazarus got to
And truss me up quick as you like. Those
Old Jesus freaks and the weathermen
Round here have been going on about
This for years. Move yourself, Greaser Boy,
Get all those crowbars your grand-dad used
To hit your mum with. I'll put a stop
To this one. I'll put his little light
Out. Before he blinds us with neon

Get all the gates closed. Get the locks on
Lads, stuff every chink in the house.
Don't let pieces of light in! Windows,
Fanlights, the lot. Moonshot, whip out, get
The boys together, Horse and his lot
And stash the loot. Any of them come
Near the walls, boiling brimstone, that's it!
Tip it on top of them, frizzle them
Up like chips. Get those three-speed crossbows
And Ye Olde Englishe Cannon and spray
It round a bit – blind his Mounted Foot
With tintacks. Put Muhammad on that
Crazy catapult, lobbing millstones.
We'll stab them with sickles, clobber them
With those spiky iron balls on string.'
'Don't panic,' said Lucifer, 'I know
This guy and his shining light. Way back
In my murky past. Can't kill him off.
Dirty tricks don't work. Just keeps coming.
Still he'd better watch out, so help me.'

. . .

Again
The light said unlock:
Said Lucifer, Who
Goes there?

A huge voice replied, the lord
Of power, of strength, that made
All things. Dukes of this dark place
Undo these gates so Christ come
In, the son of heaven's King.
With that word, hell split apart,

Burst its devil's bars; no man
Nor guard could stop the gates swing
Wide. The old religious men,
Prophets, people who had walked
In darkness, 'Behold the Lamb
Of God', with Saint John sang now.
But Lucifer could not look
At it, the light blinding him.
And along that light all those
Our Lord loved came streaming out.

WILLIAM LANGLAND

(from *The Vision of Piers Plowman*, translated
from the Middle English by Ronald Tamplin)

Based on the apocryphal stories of Christ's descent into Hell and Limbo
after his Crucifixion and before the Resurrection, in order to release
souls held captive there since the Fall of Man, when Adam disobeyed
the voice of God. 'Limbo' was thought to be a place on the border of
Hell, where dwelt the just who had died before Christ's coming, and
also unbaptized infant children. 'Harrow', in Middle English, means
'rob'.

EASTER POEM

The spring shall rouse my buried Lord,
See him evacuate the loam,
Oh man, oh man, how thin you've grown.

The sun shall summon up his own,
His gown is white, his skin is brown,
But man, oh man, how thin you've grown.

Did you suffer life in vain?
Your lips are sealed, your mind is gone,
Oh man, oh man, how thin you've grown.

Rivers have washed away his brain,
His bones are rocks, he feels no pain,
But man, oh Lord, how thin you've grown.

KATHLEEN RAINE

EASTER SUNDAY

Most glorious Lord of Life! that, on this day,
Didst make Thy triumph over death and sin:
And, having harrowed hell, didst bring away
Captivity thence captive, us to win:
This joyous day, deare Lord, with joy begin,
And grant that we, for whom thou diddest die,
Being with Thy deare blood cleane washt from sin,
May live for ever in felicity!
And that Thy love we weighing worthily,
May likewise love Thee for the same again;
And for Thy sake, that all like deare didst buy,
With love may one another entertaine!
  So let us love, deare Love, like as we ought,
  – Love is the lesson which the Lord us taught.

EDMUND SPENSER

EASTER SONG

I got me flowers to straw Thy way,
I got me boughs off many a tree;
But Thou wast up by break of day,
And brought'st Thy sweets along with Thee.

The sunne arising in the East,
Though he give light, and th' East perfume,
If they should offer to contest
With Thy arising, they presume.

Can there be any day but this,
Though many sunnes to shine endeavour?
We count three hundred, but we misse:
There is but one, and that one ever.

GEORGE HERBERT

EASTER

Break the box and shed the nard;
Stop not now to count the cost;
Hither bring pearl, opal, sard;
Reck not what the poor have lost;
Upon Christ throw all away;
Know ye, this is Easter Day.

Build His church and deck His shrine;
Empty though it be on earth;
Ye have kept your choicest wine –
Let it flow for heavenly mirth;

Pluck the harp and breathe the horn:
Know ye not 'tis Easter morn?

Gather gladness from the skies;
Take a lesson from the ground;
Flowers do ope their heavenward eyes
And a Spring-time joy have found;
Earth throws Winter's robes away,
Decks herself for Easter Day.

Beauty now for ashes wear,
Perfumes for the garb of woe.
Chaplets for dishevelled hair,
Dances for sad footsteps slow;
Open wide your hearts that they
Let in joy this Easter Day.

Seek God's house in happy throng;
Crowded let His table be;
Mingle praises, prayer and song,
Singing to the Trinity.
Henceforth let your souls alway
Make each morn an Easter Day.

GERARD MANLEY HOPKINS

nard: sweet-smelling balsam or ointment
sard: precious stone; yellow or orange cornelian

EASTER EGGS

Easter eggs! Easter eggs! Give to him that begs!
For Christ the Lord is arisen.

To the poor, open door, something give from your store!
For Christ the Lord is arisen.

Those who hoard can't afford, moth and rust their
reward!
For Christ the Lord is arisen.

Those who love freely give, long and well may they live!
For Christ the Lord is arisen.

Eastertide, like a bride, comes, and won't be denied.
For Christ the Lord is arisen.

ANONYMOUS
(translated from the traditional Russian
Easter song *Dalalin*)

THE MAY MAGNIFICAT

May is Mary's month, and I
Muse at that and wonder why:
    Her feasts follow reason,
    Dated due to season –

Candlemas, Lady Day;
But the Lady Month, May,
    Why fasten that upon her,
    With a feasting in her honour?

Is it only its being brighter
Than the most are must delight her?
   Is it opportunest
   And flowers finds soonest?

Ask of her, the mighty mother:
Her reply puts this other
   Question: What is Spring? –
   Growth in every thing –

Flesh and fleece, fur and feather,
Grass and greenworld all together;
   Star-eyed strawberry-breasted
   Throstle above her nested

Cluster of bugle blue eggs thin
Forms and warms the life within;
   And bird and blossom swell
   In sod or sheath or shell.

All things rising, all things sizing
Mary sees, sympathising
   With that world of good,
   Nature's motherhood.

Their magnifying of each its kind
With delight calls to mind
   How she did in her stored
   Magnify the Lord.

Well but there was more than this:
Spring's universal bliss
   Much, had much to say
   To offering Mary May.

When drop-of-blood-and-foam-dapple
Bloom lights the orchard-apple
  And thicket and thorp are merry
  With silver-surfèd cherry

And azuring-over greybell makes
Wood banks and brakes wash wet like lakes
  And magic cuckoocall
  Caps, clears, and clinches all –

This ecstasy all through mothering earth
Tells Mary her mirth till Christ's birth
  To remember and exultation
  In God who was her salvation.

GERARD MANLEY HOPKINS

bugle: English name for blue wild flower of the mint family

LORD JESUS! WITH WHAT SWEETNESS AND DELIGHTS

Lord Jesus ! With what sweetness and delights,
Sure, holy hopes, high joys and quick'ning flights
Dost thou feed thine ! O thou ! the hand that lifts
To him, who gives all good and perfect gifts,
Thy glorious, bright Ascension (though remov'd
So many ages from me) is so prov'd
And by thy spirit seal'd to me, that I
Feel me a sharer in thy victory.
    I soar and rise
    Up to the skies,
      Leaving the world their day,

156

And in my flight,
For the true light
Go seeking all the way;
I greet thy sepulchre, salute thy grave,
That blest enclosure, where the angels gave
The first glad tidings of thy early light,
And resurrection from the earth and night.
I see that morning in thy convert's tears,
Fresh as the dew, which but this dawning wears?
I smell her spices, and her ointment yields,
As rich a scent as the new-primros'd fields:
The day-star smiles, and light, with thee deceas'd,
Now shines in all the chambers of the east.

HENRY VAUGHAN
(from *Ascension-Day*)

MILLION-FUELÈD, NATURE'S
BONFIRE BURNS ON

Million-fuelèd, nature's bonfire burns on.
But quench her bonniest, dearest to her, her clearest-
selvèd spark
Man, how fast his firedint, his mark on mind, is gone!
Both are in an unfathomable, all is in an enormous dark
Drowned. O pity and indignation! Manshape, that shone
Sheer off, disseveral, a star, death blots black out; nor
mark
Is any of him at all so stark

157

But vastness blurs and time beats level. Enough! the
   Resurrection,
A heart's-clarion! Away grief's gasping, joyless days,
   dejection.
      Across my foundering deck shone
A beacon, an eternal beam. Flesh fade, and mortal trash
Fall to the residuary worm; world's wildfire, leave but
   ash:
      In a flash, at a trumpet crash,
I am all at once what Christ is, since he was what I am,
   and
This Jack, joke, poor potsherd, patch, matchwood,
   immortal diamond,
      Is immortal diamond.

GERARD MANLEY HOPKINS

(from *That Nature is a Heraclitean Fire
and Of the Comfort of the Resurrection*)

disseveral: a word made by combining 'dissever' (to separate or divide)
  with 'several'
residuary: still remaining
Jack: a man of the common people
potsherd: broken piece of earthenware
patch: fool; dolt

HAIL THE DAY THAT SEES HIM RISE

Hail the day that sees Him rise,
Ravish'd from our wishful eyes!
Christ, awhile to mortals given,
Re-ascends his native heaven.

There the pompous triumph waits:
'Lift your heads, eternal gates;

Wide unfold the radiant scene;
Take the King of Glory in!'

Circled round with angel powers,
Their triumphant Lord, and ours,
Conqueror over death and sin;
Take the King of Glory in!

Him though highest heaven receives,
Still he loves the earth he leaves;
Though returning to his throne,
Still he calls mankind his own.

See, he lifts his hands above!
See, he shows the prints of love!
Hark, his gracious lips bestow
Blessings on his church below!

Still for us his death he pleads;
Prevalent he intercedes;
Near himself prepares our place,
Harbinger of human race.

Master, (will we ever say,)
Taken from our head to-day;
See thy faithful servants, see,
Ever gazing up to thee.

Grant, though parted from our sight,
High above yon azure height,
Grant our hearts may thither rise,
Following thee beyond the skies.

Ever upward let us move,
Wafted on the wings of love;

Looking when our Lord shall come,
Longing, gasping after home.

There we shall with thee remain,
Partners of thy endless reign;
There thy face unclouded see,
Find our heaven of heavens in thee.

CHARLES WESLEY

MIRACLES,
PARABLES AND
MYSTERIES

FAITH, HOPE AND CHARITY

I walked the road, deep in conversation
With the two men. One was talking of faith,
The other of hope. Suddenly we saw
A Samaritan on a mule, moving
At speed in the same direction as us.
He came on the Jericho road, making
For the tournament in Jerusalem.
Together the four of us came upon
A man lying injured. Thieves had beaten
Him up and left him for dead. He couldn't
Take a step, stand up, even stir a foot
Or flex his hands. There was nothing he could
Do for himself. He seemed to be half dead,
Stripped naked as a needle, nobody
There to help him. The man who talked about
Faith had noticed him first but slipped quickly
By and wouldn't touch him with a bargepole.
The one who'd been on about hope tiptoed
Along next. He'd just been bragging about
All the people he'd helped by following
What the ten commandments said you should do.
And then he saw the man and took off past
Him, God help us! really scared, like a duck
Cringing from a falcon. But as soon as
The Samaritan saw the body there,
He dismounted and, leading his mule, went
To the man to inspect his wounds. He felt
His pulse, realized he was not far off
Dying and if he didn't get fixed up,
That was it, he'd never get up again.

So he unstrapped his bottles, opened them
Both and bathed the man's wounds with wine and oil,
Smeared him with healing ointments and bandaged
His head. Then picking him up in his arms
He put him across his mule and took him
To the farming village they call Christlaw
Six miles or so from the new market town.
He made him comfortable at the inn, called
The landlord and said, 'Look after this man
Till I get back from the tournament. Here's
The money to keep his wounds dressed.' He gave
Him enough for the expenses and said,
'If you need more I'll pay the bill later.
Now I must get on.' The Samaritan
Remounted his mule and then galloped out
At great speed on the Jerusalem road.

WILLIAM LANGLAND
(from *The Vision of Piers Plowman*,
translated from the Middle English
by Ronald Tamplin)

DIVES AND LAZARUS

As it fell out upon a day,
　　Rich Dives he made a feast,
And he invited all his friends,
　　And gentry of the best.

Then Lazarus laid him down and down,
　　And down at Dives' door:
'Some meat, some drink, brother Dives,
　　Bestow upon the poor.'

'Thou art none of my brother, Lazarus,
   That lies begging at my door;
No meat nor drink will I give thee,
   Nor bestow upon the poor.'

Then Lazarus laid him down and down,
   And down at Dives' wall:
'Some meat, some drink, brother Dives,
   Or with hunger starve I shall.'

'Thou art none of my brother, Lazarus,
   That lies begging at my wall;
No meat nor drink will I give thee,
   But with hunger starve you shall.'

Then Lazarus laid him down and down,
   And down at Dives' gate:
'Some meat, some drink, brother Dives,
   For Jesus Christ his sake.'

'Thou art none of my brother, Lazarus,
   That lies begging at my gate;
No meat nor drink will I give thee,
   For Jesus Christ his sake.'

Then Dives sent out his merry men,
   To whip poor Lazarus away;
They had no power to strike a stroke,
   But flung their whips away.

Then Dives sent out his hungry dogs,
   To bite him as he lay;
They had no power to bite at all,
   But licked his sores away.

As it fell out upon a day,
   Poor Lazarus sickened and died;
Then came two angels out of heaven
   His soul therein to guide.

'Rise up, rise up, brother Lazarus,
   And go along with me;
For you've a place prepared in heaven,
   To sit on an angel's knee.'

As it fell out upon a day,
   Rich Dives sickened and died;
Then came two serpents out of hell,
   His soul therein to guide.

'Rise up, rise up, brother Dives,
   And go with us to see
A dismal place, prepared in hell,
   From which thou canst not flee.'

Then Dives looked up with his eyes,
   And saw poor Lazarus blest:
'Give me one drop of water, brother Lazarus,
   To quench my flaming thirst.

'Oh had I as many years to abide
   As there are blades of grass,
Then there would be an end, but now
   Hell's pains will ne'er be past.

'Oh was I now but alive again,
   The space of one half hour!
Oh that I had my peace secure!
   Then the devil should have no power.'

ANONYMOUS

FISHERS

That Sunday morning, the moon still high
over the town, blessing the lapping water,
we left the harbour mouth in Peter's boat,
rounded the point, then steered
for the open sea, engines
purring like contented cats.
A steady five knots we made, were well out
in the grounds by sunrise, gulls following,
a white cloud of witnesses.

Sleep in our eyes we dropped nets, trawled
an hour or so, the wind keen,
it seemed we had no hands.
We landed mackerel twice from a small shoal,
a few dabs, a dogfish or two,
nothing to boast about, but a fair catch.
By seven the moon had gone, the sun
stroked sea and sky, there was no swell;
we tried again, no fish, decided to return,
breakfast waiting at home, the family fire.

Then Peter spotted something in the net
we had not bargained for, an old iron chest,
deeper than long, rounded at the top,
rusted and green, bound with two clasps.
Andrew, our skipper, laid it on the deck,
swimming with water and scales, we stared,
wondering what the strange box held;
We forgot the fish in the hold, the wind
salting our skins, our eyes
sharp as diamonds.

166

The keyhole was stopped with mud, broken shell,
the clasps soon gave, the lock held fast;
Peter broke it with a gutting knife,
gasped, raised his eyes to heaven,
lifted out two silver plates,
tarnished by time, a burnished cup
with delicate, figured stem,
and last, a jewelled crucifix,
that glittered in the first-day sun,
ruby and amethyst, a holy sight.
Then Peter raised the cross on high,
we had no words, but thought
we heard the church bells on the land,
ringing for early service. Turned about,
chugged back home.

It was a nine day's wonder,
we told the tale a hundred times,
though Andrew kept his peace;
Peter only smiled
when people questioned him.

We later learned the silver and the gold
were Mexican, the treasure we had found,
from a great galleon, wrecked
upon our needle coasts, intended
for some English church by priests
who sailed with that proud fleet
and longed to hear the Mass said once again.

Now above the altar of our church
the jewelled cross shines, the cup and plates
are used, the old faith with the new.

LEONARD CLARK

JUDAS ISCARIOT

'Twas the soul of Judas Iscariot,
    Strange, and sad, and tall,
Stood all alone at dead of night
    Before a lighted hall.

And the wold was white with snow,
    And his foot-marks black and damp,
And the ghost of the silvern Moon arose,
    Holding her yellow lamp.

And the icicles were on the eaves,
    And the walls were deep with white,
And the shadows of the guests within
    Pass'd on the window light.

The shadows of the wedding guests
    Did strangely come and go,
And the body of Judas Iscariot
    Lay stretch'd along the snow.

The body of Judas Iscariot
    Lay stretch'd along the snow;
'Twas the soul of Judas Iscariot
    Ran swiftly to and fro.

To and fro, and up and down,
    He ran so swiftly there,
As round and round the frozen Pole
    Glideth the lean white bear.

... 'Twas the Bridegroom sat at the table-head,
    And the lights burnt bright and clear –
'Oh, who is that,' the Bridegroom said,
    'Whose weary feet I hear?'

'Twas one look'd from the lighted hall,
    And answer'd soft and slow,
'It is a wolf runs up and down
    With a black track in the snow.'

The Bridegroom in his robe of white
    Sat at the table-head –
'Oh, who is that who moans without?'
    The blessèd Bridegroom said.

'Twas one look'd from the lighted hall,
    And answer'd fierce and low,
''Tis the soul of Judas Iscariot
    Gliding to and fro.'

'Twas the soul of Judas Iscariot
    Did hush itself and stand,
And saw the Bridegroom at the door
    With a light in his hand.

The Bridegroom stood in the open door,
    And he was clad in white,
And far within the Lord's Supper
    Was spread so broad and bright.

The Bridegroom shaded his eyes and look'd,
    And his face was bright to see –
'What dost thou here at the Lord's Supper
    With thy body's sins?' said he.

'Twas the soul of Judas Iscariot
    Stood black, and sad, and bare –
'I have wander'd many nights and days;
    There is no light elsewhere.'

'Twas the wedding guests cried out within,
    And their eyes were fierce and bright –
'Scourge the soul of Judas Iscariot
    Away into the night!'

The Bridegroom stood in the open door,
    And he waved hands still and slow,
And the third time that he waved his hands
    The air was thick with snow.

And of every flake of falling snow,
    Before it touch'd the ground,
There came a dove, and a thousand doves
    Made sweet sound.

'Twas the body of Judas Iscariot
    Floated away full fleet,
And the wings of the doves that bare it off
    Were like its winding-sheet.

'Twas the Bridegroom stood at the open door,
    And beckon'd, smiling sweet;
'Twas the soul of Judas Iscariot
    Stole in, and fell at his feet.

'The Holy Supper is spread within,
    And the many candles shine,
And I have waited long for thee
    Before I pour'd the wine!'

The supper wine is pour'd at last,
    The lights burn bright and fair,
Iscariot washes the Bridegroom's feet,
    And dries them with his hair.

ROBERT WILLIAMS BUCHANAN

A BALLAD OF SAINT JOHN'S MORNING

(*Manhaninha de S. Joâo*)

'Twas on a morning of Saint John
When scarce had dawned the day,
Christ Jesus walked beside a stream
And these words did He say:

'Blessèd be thou, fair rivulet,
And holy, from this hour.'
Hard by the daughter of a king
Listened within her tower.

Swiftly she donned her silken hose
And silver shoes a-gleam,
And ran with jar of gold to draw
Fresh water from the stream.

As she drew near the rivulet
Our Lady she espied:
'O Virgin Mother, tell me true
If e'er I'll be a bride!'

'Happily, daughter, wilt thou wed
And bear fine sons withal;
One will become the Pope of Rome,
And one a cardinal.

The youngest all his days will spend
In serving me, I deem.
Go, lucky damosel, and fill
Thy pitcher from the stream!'

ANONYMOUS
(translated from the Portuguese by
Norma Douglas Henry)

ONE FEBRUARY,
THERE CAME AN AFTERNOON

One February, there came an afternoon
when the hill villages and fields around the convent
   shone
painted with light. Each cypress threw its shadow; the
   clear
young blue of the sky was shrill with larks. In this
   springtime of the year
the brothers took their recreation out of doors
(they needed recreation just as you need yours)
in the long day of work and prayer, an hour's welcome
   pause.

They walked down the lane, chattering at their ease
and watching the wind blow green and silver in the olive
   trees,
when all at once there came a dreadsome sound
that broke the air and shook the ground,
rolling from hill to hill; it seemed to hem
the world in thunder and, onto that quiet path that led to
   Bethlehem,
a great maned lion stepped, not twenty yards from them.

Prrt! The brothers scattered like swallows: their cries
   came
back on the wind as they ran, calling sweet Mary's name
to save them. Nor did one wait
to help another but, pell-mell, in at the gate
they tumbled, and slammed it fast with bolt and lock.
Saint Jerome was left outside; unmoved as a rock
he stayed as a good shepherd stays who has to guard his
   flock.

'God be with me,' he prayed, but still the lion came on,
roaring to split the sky, but now his tone
seemed to the Saint more hurt than angry; and then he
    saw
this lion limped on three legs, one front paw
hung swollen, bleeding, and misery
had so furrowed his face that the Saint could see
he had not come to devour but to ask for charity.

For three nights and days the lion had not slept.
His flanks were thin, his gold eyes wept
as he wandered in pain and fever, roaring, as if asking
    why
a lion should suffer. 'A weasel or goat or bad serpent, but
    I,
the King of Beasts, to find a thorn such woe!'
(He had fallen into a thicket of thorns a week ago
and one had festered.) All this Saint Jerome seemed to
    know,

and laid his hand on the hot snuff-coloured brow.
'Lord Jesus is the King of Kings,' he said, 'but I shall
    read you how
He suffered with a hundred thorn wreath pricks.'
The lion listened thoughtfully, gave the hand lion licks
to show his pity, and tried to sink his roaring to a
    moan.
'Lord Jesus! Then His beast is not alone,'
and he limped up to the convent gate with Saint Jerome.

They knocked,
and smiled at one another now to find it locked.
The brothers opened trembling, but when they saw
    Jerome come
walking in with the lion, they were dumb

with amazement – and shame at leaving their master
  outside.
'Punish us,' they implored him, but Jerome only cried,
'Bring herbs, hot water, linen.' Then, with as much fuss,
  as if a pride

of lions were wounded, they set about
bathing the paw. First they pulled the long thorn out.
The operation was painful, the lion could not help a
  howl,
which, looking up into Jerome's face, he hastily sank to a
  growl,
and, as pus streamed out, to a whimper;
then, when the paw was poulticed and dressed, came a
  sound that made a stir
through the whole convent: a contented happy rumbling
  that was the lion's purr.

A gentle time passed that helped to heal the paw.
The lion was given a cell with a bed of the cleanest straw,
and kept the convent hours and shared the convent food.
When the brothers sang in choir or said their Mass, he
  stood
quiet outside the chapel door, or else he lay
with his front paws put together, as if to say,
'I am a Christian lion now and I too can pray.'

RUMER GODDEN
(from *St Jerome and the Lion*)

St Jerome (c. 342 – 420), one of the four great Latin Doctors of the Church,
  was educated in Rome. From the year 386 he lived in Bethlehem. He
  translated almost the whole of the Bible from Hebrew and Greek into
  Latin. This version, in the ordinary ('vulgar') Latin speech of the common
  people, became known as the Vulgate.

THE MAID AND THE PALMER

The maid she went to the well to washe,
Dew fell off her lily-white fleshe.

White she washte, and white she rong,
White she hang'd on the hazel wand.

There came an old palmer by the way,
Says, 'God speed thee well, thou fair may.

'Has tow either cup or can,
To give an old palmer drink therein?'

Says, 'I have neither cup nor can,
To give an old palmer drink therein.'

'But an thy leman come from Rome,
Cups and cans thou wilt find soon.'

She swore by God and good Saint John
Leman she had never none.

Says, 'Peace, fair maid, you are forsworne,
Ninè children you have borne.

'Three were buryed under thy bed's head,
Other three under thy brewing lead.

'Other three play on yon greene;
Count, maid, and there be nine.' –

'But I hope you are the good old man
That all the world beleeves upon.

'Old palmer, I pray thee,
Penaunce that thou wilt give to me.' –

'Penaunce I can give thee none
But seven year to be a stepping-stone.

'Other seven a clapper in a bell,
Other seven to lead an ape in hell.

'When thou has thy penaunce done,
Then thou'st come a mayden home.'

ANONYMOUS

palmer: an itinerant monk who has taken a vow of poverty; a pilgrim
  returning from the Holy Land with a palm leaf or branch as a sign that
  he has been there
may: maiden; virgin
leman: lover
brewing lead: large, open vat used in brewing beer, originally made of lead

OH! ST PATRICK WAS A GENTLEMAN

Oh! St Patrick was a gentleman,
    Who came of decent people;
He built a church in Dublin town,
    And put on it a steeple.
His father was a Gallagher,
    His mother was a Brady;
His aunt was an O'Shaughnessy,
    His uncle an O'Grady.
            So, Success attend St Patrick's fist,
                For he's a saint so clever;
                Oh! he gave the snakes and toads a twist,
                He bothered them for ever!

The Wicklow hills are very high,
    And so's the Hill of Howth, sir;

But there's a hill, much bigger still,
    Much higher nor them both, sir.
'Twas on the top of this high hill
    St Patrick preached his sarmint,
That drove the frogs into the bogs,
    And banished all the varmint.
          Oh, Success, &c.

There's not a mile in Ireland's isle
    Where dirty varmin musters,
But there he put his dear fore-foot,
    And murdered them in clusters.
The toads went pop, the frogs went hop,
    Slap dash into the water,
And the snakes committed suicide
    To save themselves from slaughter.
          Oh, Success, &c.

Nine hundred thousand reptiles blue
    He charmed them with sweet discourses,
And dined on them at Killaloe
    In soups and second courses.
Where blind worms crawling in the glass
    Disgusted all the nation,
He gave them a rise, which opened their eyes
    To a sense of their situation.
          Oh, Success, &c.

No wonder that those Irish lads
    Should be so gay and frisky,
For sure St Pat, he taught them that,
    As well as making whiskey;
No wonder that the Saint himself
    Should understand distilling,

177

Since his mother kept a shebeen shop
    In the town of Enniskillen.
        Oh, Success, &c.

Oh! was I but so fortunate
    As to be back in Munster,
'Tis I'd be bound, that from that ground
    I never more would once stir.
For there St Patrick planted turf,
    And plenty of the praties;
With pigs *galore, ma gra, ma'store,*
    And cabbages, – and ladies.
Then my blessing on St Patrick's fist,
    For he's the darling Saint, O!
Oh, he gave the snakes and toads a twist,
    He's a beauty without paint, O!

ANONYMOUS

ma gra, ma'store: my love, my treasure

LEGEND

The blacksmith's boy went out with a rifle
and a black dog running behind.
Cobwebs snatched at his feet,
rivers hindered him,
thorn branches caught at his eyes to make him blind
and the sky turned into an unlucky opal,
but he didn't mind,
I can break branches, I can swim rivers, I can stare out
    any spider I meet,
Said he to his dog and his rifle.

The blacksmith's boy went over the paddocks
with his old black hat on his head.
Mountains jumped in his way,
rocks rolled down on him,
and the old crow cried, 'You'll soon be dead.'
And the rain came down like mattocks.
But he only said
I can climb mountains, I can dodge rocks, I can shoot an
    old crow any day,
and he went on over the paddocks.

When he came to the end of the day the sun began
    falling.
Up came the night ready to swallow him,
like the barrel of a gun,
like an old black hat,
like a black dog hungry to follow him.
Then the pigeon, the magpie and the dove began wailing
and the grass lay down to pillow him.
His rifle broke, his hat blew away and his dog was gone
and the sun was falling.

But in front of the night the rainbow stood on the
    mountain,
just as his heart foretold.
He ran like a hare,
he climbed like a fox;
he caught it in his hands, the colours and the cold –
like a bar of ice, like the column of a fountain,
like a ring of gold.
The pigeon, the magpie and the dove flew up to stare,
and the grass stood up again on the mountain.

The blacksmith's boy hung the rainbow on his shoulder
instead of his broken gun.
Lizards ran out to see,
snakes made way for him,
and the rainbow shone as brightly as the sun.
All the world said, Nobody is braver, nobody is bolder,
nobody else has done
anything to equal it. He went home as bold as he could be
with the swinging rainbow on his shoulder.

JUDITH WRIGHT

opal: semi-precious stone, thought by some to bring ill-luck to the wearer
paddocks: here used in the Australian sense of extensive pasture land
mattock: agricultural tool like a pick-axe, with one end having a flat blade
    similar to an adze, and used for breaking up hard ground

SAINTS AND PROPHETS

ST FRANCIS AND THE BIRDS

When Francis preached love to the birds
They listened, fluttered, throttled up
Into the blue like a flock of words

Released for fun from his holy lips.
Then wheeled back, whirred about his head,
Pirouetted on brothers' capes,

Danced on the wing, for sheer joy played
And sang, like images took flight.
Which was the best poem Francis made,

His argument true, his tone light.

SEAMUS HEANEY

ST STEPHEN AND KING HEROD

Saint Stephen was a clerk
  In King Herod's hall,
And servèd him of bread and cloth
  As every king befall.

Stephen out of kitchen came
  With boar's head on hand,
He saw a star was fair and bright
  Over Bethlehem stand.

He cast adown the boar's head
  And went into the hall;
'I forsake thee, Herod,
  And thy workès all.

'I forsake thee, King Herod,
  And thy workès all,
There is a child in Bethlehem born
  Is better than we all.' –

'What aileth thee, Stephen?
  What is thee befall?
Lacketh thee either meat or drink
  In King Herod's hall?' –

'Lacketh me neither meat ne drink
  In King Herod's hall;
There is a child in Bethlehem born
  Is better than we all.' –

'What aileth thee, Stephen?
  Art wode or 'ginnest to brede?

Lacketh thee either gold or fee,
    Or any rich weed?' –

'Lacketh me neither gold ne fee
    Ne none rich weed;
There is a child in Bethlehem born
    Shall helpen us at our need.' –

'That is all so sooth, Stephen,
    All so sooth, I-wys,
As this capon crowè shall
    That li'th here in my dish.'

That word was not so soon said,
    That word in that hall,
The capon crew *Christus natus est*
    Among the lordès all.

'Risit up, my tormentors,
    By two and all by one,
And leadit Stephen out of this town,
    And stonit him with stone.'

Tooken they Stephen
    And stoned him in the way;
And therefore is his even
    On Christe's own day.

ANONYMOUS

clerk: in this sense, household servant
wode: mad
'ginnest to brede: starting to become (mad)
weed: clothing
sooth: true
I-wys: certainly
capon: castrated cock or rooster fattened for eating

MAGDALEN AT MICHAEL'S GATE

Magdalen at Michael's gate
    Tirled at the pin;
On Joseph's thorn sang the blackbird,
    'Let her in! Let her in!'

'Hast thou seen the wounds?' said Michael,
    'Know'st thou thy sin?'
'It is evening, evening,' sang the blackbird,
    'Let her in! Let her in!'

'Yes, I have seen the wounds,
    And I know my sin.'
'She knows it well, well, well,' sang the blackbird,
    'Let her in! Let her in!'

'Thou bringest no offerings,' said Michael.
    'Nought save sin.'
And the blackbird sang, 'She is sorry, sorry, sorry,
    Let her in! Let her in!'

When he had sung himself to sleep,
    And night did begin,
One came and opened Michael's gate,
    And Magdalen went in.

HENRY KINGSLEY
(from the novel *The Boy in Grey*)

BAR THE DOOR. BAR THE DOOR.

(*In Canterbury Cathedral.* ARCHBISHOP
THOMAS BECKET *and* PRIESTS)

PRIESTS : Bar the door. Bar the door.
  The door is barred.
  We are safe. We are safe.
  They dare not break in.
  They cannot break in. They have not the force.
  We are safe. We are safe.
THOMAS: Unbar the doors! throw open the doors!
  I will not have the house of prayer, the church of
    Christ,
  The sanctuary, turned into a fortress.
  The Church shall protect her own, in her own way,
    not
  As oak and stone; stone and oak decay,
  Give no stay, but the Church shall endure.
  The Church shall be open, even to our enemies. Open
    the door!
PRIESTS: My Lord! these are not men, these come not as
    men come, but
  Like maddened beasts. They come not like men, who
  Respect the sanctuary, who kneel to the Body of
    Christ,
  But like beasts. You would bar the door
  Against the lion, the leopard, the wolf or the boar,
  Why not more
  Against beasts with the souls of damned men, against
    men
  Who would damn themselves to beasts. My Lord! My
    Lord!

THOMAS: You think me reckless, desperate and mad.
  You argue by results, as this world does,
  To settle if an act be good or bad.
  You defer to the fact. For every life and every act
  Consequence of good and evil can be shown.
  And as in time results of many deeds are blended
  So good and evil in the end become confounded.
  It is not in time that my death shall be known;
  It is out of time that my decision is taken
  If you call that decision
  To which my whole being gives entire consent.
  I give my life
  To the Law of God above the Law of Man.
  Unbar the door! unbar the door!
  We are not here to triumph by fighting, by stratagem,
      or by resistance,
  Not to fight with beasts as men. We have fought the
      beast
  And have conquered. We have only to conquer
  Now, by suffering. This is the easier victory.
  Now is the triumph of the Cross, now
  Open the door! I command it. OPEN THE DOOR!
(*The door is opened. The* KNIGHTS *enter, slightly tipsy*)
PRIESTS: This way, my Lord! Quick. Up the stair. To
      the roof.
  To the crypt. Quick. Come. Force him.
KNIGHTS : Where is Becket, the traitor to the King?
      Where is Becket, the meddling priest?
  Come down Daniel to the lions' den,
      Come down Daniel for the mark of the beast.

  Are you washed in the blood of the Lamb?
      Are you marked with the mark of the beast?

187

Come down Daniel to the lions' den,
   Come down Daniel and join in the feast.

Where is Becket the Cheapside brat?
   Where is Becket the faithless priest?
Come down Daniel to the lions' den,
   Come down Daniel and join in the feast.

THOMAS: It is the just man who
Like a bold lion, should be without fear.
I am here.
No traitor to the King. I am a priest,
A Christian, saved by the blood of Christ,
Ready to suffer with my blood.
This is the sign of the Church always,
The sign of blood. Blood for blood.
His blood given to buy my life,
My blood given to pay for His death,
My death for His death.

FIRST KNIGHT: Absolve all those you have
   excommunicated.

SECOND KNIGHT: Resign the powers you have
   arrogated.

THIRD KNIGHT: Restore to the King the money you
   appropriated.

FIRST KNIGHT: Renew the obedience you have
   violated.

THOMAS: For my Lord I am now ready to die,
That his Church may have peace and liberty.
Do with me as you will, to your hurt and shame;
But none of my people, in God's name,
Whether layman or clerk, shall you touch.
This I forbid.

KNIGHTS: Traitor! traitor! traitor!

THOMAS: You, Reginald, three times traitor you:
  Traitor to me as my temporal vassal,
  Traitor to me as your spiritual lord,
  Traitor to God in desecrating His Church.
FIRST KNIGHT: No faith do I owe to a renegade,
  And what I owe shall now be paid.
THOMAS: Now to Almighty God, to the Blessed Mary
  ever Virgin, to the blessed John the Baptist, the holy
  apostles Peter and Paul, to the blessed martyr Denys,
  and to all the Saints, I commend my cause and that of
  the Church.
(*The* KNIGHTS *kill him.*)

T. S. ELIOT
(from *Murder in the Cathedral*)

WE SHALL GO AS FAR AS
THE WITHIES TAKE US

(CUTHMAN – *afterwards* ST CUTHMAN – *has set off on a journey across South England. He has a rope of withies fastened from the cart to his shoulder. His widowed mother is travelling with him.*)

CUTHMAN: We shall go as far
As the withies take us. There, where they break,
Where God breaks them, you shall set up
House again and put clean paper on
Larder shelves. And there where God breaks them
And scoops our peace out of a strange field
I shall build my answer in plank and brick,
Labour out my thanks in plaster and beam
And stone. You, Mother, and I, when God
Brings our settled days again, will build
A church where the withies are broken, a church to
   pray in
When you have put your broom away, and untied
Your apron.
MOTHER: Build a church, with our own hands?
CUTHMAN: With our own hands, Mother, and with our
   own
Love of God and with nothing else; for I have
Nothing else; I have no craft or knowledge of joint
Or strain, more than will make a cart, and even
The cart you scarcely would call handsome. What
Did I learn to do after I found my feet
And found my tongue? Only to seem as intelligent
As the neighbours' children whatever happened; to be

Always a little less than myself in order
To avoid being conspicuous. But now
I am less than I would be, less
Than I must be; my buzzing life is less
Than my birth was or my death will be. The church
And I shall be built together; and together
Find our significance. Breaking and building
In the progression of this world go hand in hand.
And where the withies break I shall build.

MOTHER: I am always lagging a little behind your
    thoughts,
I am always put out of breath by them. No doubt
I shall arrive one of these days.

CUTHMAN: In, Mother.
We shall arrive together if the cart holds good.

MOTHER: It always seems to me I take my life
In my hands, every time I get into this
Contraption.

CUTHMAN: Listen to that! A hard week's work
And she calls it a contraption!

(*They set out again.*)

CHRISTOPHER FRY
(from *The Boy with a Cart*)

St Cuthman is thought to have lived in the ninth century and to have
built a small church, helped by friends, at Steyning in Suffolk.

ST JOHN THE BAPTIST

The last and greatest herald of heaven's king,
Girt with rough skins, hies to the deserts wild,
Among that savage brood the woods forth bring
Which he than man more harmless found and mild:

His food was locusts, and what young doth spring,
With honey that from virgin hives distilled;
Parched body, hollow eyes, some uncouth thing
Made him appear long since from earth exiled.

There burst he forth: 'All ye, whose hopes rely
On God, with me amidst these deserts mourn;
Repent, repent, and from old errors turn.'
Who listened to his voice, obeyed his cry?

    Only the echoes which he made relent,
    Rung from their marble caves, *Repent, repent*.

WILLIAM DRUMMOND

JOHN THE BAPTIST

    The water
    of the world
    is love

    The Water
    of the World
    is Love

    SAMUEL MENASHE

GOD'S CHILDREN

ON ZACHEUS

Me thinks, I see, with what a busy haste,
Zacheus climb'd the Tree: But O, how fast,
How full of speed, canst thou imagine (when
Our Saviour call'd) he powder'd down agen!
He ne'er made trial, if the boughs were sound,
Or rotten; nor how far 'twas to the ground:
There was no danger fear'd; at such a Call,
He'll venture nothing, that dare fear a fall;
Needs must be down, by such a Spirit driven,
Nor could he fall unless he fall to Heaven.
Down came Zacheus, ravisht from the tree;
Bird that was shot ne'er dropt so quick as he.

FRANCIS QUARLES

powder'd: rushed impetuously
ravisht: entranced; carried away with strong feelings

MRS MALONE

Mrs Malone
Lived hard by a wood
All on her lonesome
As nobody should.
With her crust on a plate
And her pot on the coal
And none but herself
To converse with, poor soul.
In a shawl and a hood

She got sticks out-o'-door,
On a bit of old sacking
She slept on the floor,
And nobody, nobody
Asked how she fared
Or knew how she managed,
For nobody cared.
 Why make a pother
 About an old crone?
 What for should they bother
 With Mrs Malone?

One Monday in winter
With snow on the ground
So thick that a footstep
Fell without sound,
She heard a faint frostbitten
Peck on the pane
And went to the window
To listen again.
There sat a cock-sparrow
Bedraggled and weak,
With half-open eyelid
And ice on his beak.
She threw up the sash
And she took the bird in,
And mumbled and fumbled it
Under her chin.
 'Ye're all of a smother,
 Ye're fair overblown!
 I've room fer another,'
 Said Mrs Malone.

Come Tuesday while eating
Her dry morning slice
With the sparrow a-picking
('Ain't company nice!')
She heard on her doorpost
A curious scratch,
And there was a cat
With its claw on the latch.
It was hungry and thirsty
And thin as a lath,
It mewed and it mowed
On the slithery path.
She threw the door open
And warmed up some pap,
And huddled and cuddled it
In her old lap.
      'There, there, little brother,
      Ye poor skin-an'-bone,
      There's room fer another,'
      Said Mrs Malone.

Come Wednesday while all of them
Crouched on the mat
With a crumb for the sparrow,
A sip for the cat,
There was wailing and whining
Outside in the wood,
And there sat a vixen
With six of her brood.
She was haggard and ragged
And worn to a shred,
And her half-dozen babies

Were only half-fed,
But Mrs Malone, crying
'My! ain't they sweet!'
Happed them and lapped them
And gave them to eat.
    'You warm yerself, mother,
    Ye're cold as a stone!
    There's room fer another,'
    Said Mrs Malone.

Come Thursday a donkey
Stepped in off the road
With sores on his withers
From bearing a load.
Come Friday when icicles
Pierced the white air
Down from the mountainside
Lumbered a bear.
For each she had something,
If little, to give –
'Lord knows, the poor critters
Must all of 'em live.'
She gave them her sacking,
Her hood and her shawl,
Her loaf and her teapot –
She gave them her all.
    'What with one thing and t'other
    Me fambily's grown,
    And there's room fer another,'
    Said Mrs Malone.

Come Saturday evening
When time was to sup

Mrs Malone
Had forgot to sit up.
The cat said *meeow*,
And the sparrow said *peep*,
The vixen, *she's sleeping*,
The bear, *let her sleep*.
On the back of the donkey
They bore her away,
Through trees and up mountains
Beyond night and day,
Till come Sunday morning
They brought her in state
Through the last cloudbank
As far as the Gate.
    'Who is it,' asked Peter,
    'You have with you there?'
    And donkey and sparrow,
    Cat, vixen and bear

Exclaimed, 'Do you tell us
Up here she's unknown?
It's our mother, God bless us!
It's Mrs Malone
Whose havings were few
And whose holding was small
And whose heart was so big
It had room for us all.'
Then Mrs Malone
Of a sudden awoke,
She rubbed her two eyeballs
And anxiously spoke:
'Where am I, to goodness,
And what do I see?

My dears, let's turn back,
This ain't no place fer me!'
    But Peter said, 'Mother
    Go in to the Throne.
    There's room for another
    One, Mrs Malone.'

ELEANOR FARJEON

THIS ABOVE ALL IS PRECIOUS

This above all is precious and remarkable
How we put ourselves in one another's care,
How in spite of everything, we trust each other.

Fishermen at whatever point they are dipping and lifting
On the dark green swell they partly think of as home
Hear the gale warnings that fly to them like gulls.

The scientists study the weather for love of studying it,
And not specially for love of the fishermen,
And the wireless engineers do the transmission for love
   of wireless,

But how it adds up is that when the terrible white malice
Of the waves high as cliffs is let loose to seek a victim
The fishermen are somewhere else and so not drowned.

JOHN WAIN

THE THREE HERMITS

Three old hermits took the air
By a cold and desolate sea,
First was muttering a prayer,
Second rummaged for a flea;
On a windy stone, the third,
Giddy with his hundredth year,
Sang unnoticed like a bird:
'Though the Door of Death is near
And what waits behind the door,
Three times in a single day
I, though upright on the shore,
Fall asleep when I should pray.'
So the first, but now the second:
'We're but given what we have earned
When all thoughts and deeds are reckoned,
So it's plain to be discerned
That the shades of holy men
Who have failed, being weak of will,
Pass the Door of Birth again,
And are plagued by crowds, until
They've the passion to escape.'
Moaned the other, 'They are thrown
Into some most fearful shape.'
But the second mocked his moan:
'They are not changed to anything,
Having loved God once, but maybe
To a poet or a king
Or a witty lovely lady.'
While he'd rummaged rags and hair,

Caught and cracked his flea, the third,
Giddy with his hundredth year,
Sang unnoticed like a bird.

W. B. YEATS

THE BALLAD OF FATHER GILLIGAN

The old priest Peter Gilligan
Was weary night and day;
For half his flock were in their beds,
Or under green sods lay.

Once, while he nodded on a chair,
At the moth-hour of eve,
Another poor man sent for him,
And he began to grieve.

'I have no rest, nor joy, nor peace,
For people die and die';
And after cried he, 'God forgive!
My body spake, not I!'

He knelt, and leaning on the chair
He prayed and fell asleep;
And the moth-hour went from the fields,
And stars began to peep.

They slowly into millions grew,
And leaves shook in the wind;
And God covered the world with shade,
And whispered to mankind.

Upon the time of sparrow-chirp
When the moths came once more,
The old priest Peter Gilligan
Stood upright on the floor.

'Mavrone, mavrone! the man has died
While I slept on the chair';
He roused his horse out of its sleep,
And rode with little care.

He rode now as he never rode,
By rocky lane and fen;
The sick man's wife opened the door:
'Father! you come again!'

'And is the poor man dead?' he cried.
'He died an hour ago.'
The old priest Peter Gilligan
In grief swayed to and fro.

'When you were gone, he turned and died
As merry as a bird.'
The old priest Peter Gilligan
He knelt him at that word.

'He Who hath made the night of stars
For souls who tire and bleed,
Sent one of His great angels down
To help me in my need.

'He Who is wrapped in purple robes,
With planets in His care,
Had pity on the least of things
Asleep upon a chair.'

mavrone: alas   W.B. YEATS

DUBLIN NEWSBOY IN THE SNOW

Huddling in the contracting cage
    of that outside air,
enclosed by shooting boundaries
    of cosy cars
    a lean boy,
weaned from unattainable hopes
    and distant glitters,
dips within himself to God
    but hears no reply.
Instead, only
    the passive descent of snow
covers his face with placid kisses.
    He crouches
with his sodden ware,
    crushing some snow into balls,
wishing, wishing,
    but not daring
to hurl them at the passersby,
    whirling like the snow
by his passing world.

GOH POH SENG

BULLOCKY

Beside his heavy-shouldered team,
thirsty with drought and chilled with rain,
he weathered all the striding years
till they ran widdershins in his brain:

Till the long solitary tracks
etched deeper with each lurching load
were populous before his eyes,
and fiends and angels used his road.

All the long straining journey grew
a mad apocalyptic dream,
and he old Moses, and the slaves
his suffering and stubborn team.

Then in his evening camp beneath
the half-light pillars of the trees
he filled the steepled cone of night
with shouted prayers and prophecies.

While past the campfire's crimson ring
the star-struck darkness cupped him round,
and centuries of cattlebells
rang with their sweet uneasy sound.

Grass is across the waggon-tracks,
and plough strikes bone beneath the grass,
and vineyards cover all the slopes
where the dead teams were used to pass.

O vine, grow close upon that bone
and hold it with your rooted hand.
The prophet Moses feeds the grape,
and fruitful is the Promised Land.

JUDITH WRIGHT

bullocky: bullock-driver; teamster (Australian)
widdershins: contrariwise; in a direction opposite to that of the apparent
   path of the sun, or as a clock whose hands move backwards

SUNDAY

My mother's strongest religious feeling
Was that Catholics were a sinister lot;
She would hardly trust even a lapsed one.
My father was a lapsed Catholic.

Yet we were sent to Sunday school.
Perhaps in the spirit that others
Were sent to public schools. It
Might come in useful later on.

In Sunday school a sickly adult
Taught the teachings of a sickly lamb
To a gathering of sickly children.

It was a far cry from that brisk person
Who created the heaven and the earth in
Six days and then took Sunday off.

The churches were run by a picked crew
Of bad actors radiating insincerity.
Not that one thought of them in that way,
One merely disliked the sound of their voices.
I cannot recall one elevated moment in church,
Though as a choirboy I pulled in a useful
Sixpence per month.

Strange, that a sense of religion should
Somehow survive all this grim buffoonery!
Perhaps that brisk old person does exist,
And we are living through his Sunday.

D. J. ENRIGHT

205

THE NOVICE

She turns her head demurely. In a year
Or two she will
Be able to smile openly at all.
She once enjoyed so much. Now there's a wall,
Also a grille.
Only the narrow, indoor things are clear.

She is not certain yet if she will stay.
She watches those
Who have been living here for many years.
No doubt upon each timeless face appears.
These stayed and chose
And in their suffering learnt how to pray.

Upon her window-sill two turtle doves
Gently demur.
All of the noisy world is here brought low
To these quiet birds who come and go
And seem to her
So far removed from all she hates and loves.

ELIZABETH JENNINGS

COUNTRY NUN

In a café under a lazy fan
she talks with her brother,
the breath of cows upon him,
a line of sun and hat across his brow.
Wimpled above the steak and peas,

she drifts away / drifts back,
floating as she did
in cowfields of their childhood,
lingering on the few books in the living room,
always last to the pool.

From rough-sawn walls
beyond the memory of decision
she moves through knee-high pastures
to a convent gate
farewell.

Soon now
he will need to walk her back,
feeling her lift already
towards the pure insistence
of the bell.

GEOFF PAGE

A LOCAL PREACHER'S GOODBYE

'I'll meet you again up there' –
He pointed to the smoke
With black umbrella finger
(The chimneys tall as hymns,
Fuming with extemporary prayer) –
'I'll see you all up there,'
                He said.

Six boys or seven
In the dark October drizzle,
Class tickets in our pockets,

207

Ready to leave Heaven
Locked in with the hymn-books;
Supper and bed
Hard on by the Market Clock –
'Good night, Mr Fawcett, sir,'
           We said.

Forty years of soot and rain;
A Bible-insured
Ghost of chapel steward
And manufacturer of aerated waters,
With grey-ginger beard
Bubbling my unwritten poetry –
'Grand seeing you again!',
           I say.

NORMAN NICHOLSON

PEACE
AND
WAR

PEACE

I sought for Peace, but could not find;
    I sought it in the city,
But they were of another mind,
    The more's the pity!

I sought for Peace of country swain,
    But yet I could not find;
So I, returning home again,
    Left Peace behind.

Sweet Peace, where dost thou dwell? said I.
    Methought a voice was given:
'Peace dwelt not here, long since did fly
    To God in heaven.'

Thought I, this echo is but vain,
    To folly 'tis of kin;
Anon I heard it tell me plain,
    'Twas killed by sin.

Then I believed the former voice,
    And rested well content,
Laid down and slept, rose, did rejoice,
    And then to heaven went.
There I enquired for Peace, and found it true,
An heavenly plant it was, and sweetly grew.

SAMUEL SPEED

PEACE

My soul, there is a country
  Far beyond the stars,
Where stands a wingèd sentry
  All skilful in the wars:
There, above noise and danger,
  Sweet Peace sits crown'd with smiles,
And One born in a manger
  Commands the beauteous files.
He is thy gracious Friend,
  And – O my soul, awake! –
Did in pure love descend
  To die here for thy sake.
If thou canst get but thither,
  There grows the flower of Peace,
The Rose that cannot wither,
  Thy fortress and thy ease.
Leave then thy foolish ranges;
  For none can thee secure
But One who never changes –
  Thy God, thy life, thy cure.

HENRY VAUGHAN

WITH BANNERS FURLED, AND CLARIONS MUTE

With banners furled, and clarions mute,
  An army passes in the night;
And beaming spears and helms salute
  The dark with bright.

In silence deep the legions stream,
    With open ranks, in order true;
Over boundless plains they stream and gleam –
    No chief in view!

Afar, in twinkling distance lost,
    (So legends tell) he lonely wendᶜ
And back through all that shining host
    His mandate sends.

HERMAN MELVILLE

THE TURTLE DOVE

One day, one day,
After the eagles of war have preyed,
When the flowers appear on the earth, and it is spring –
The time of the singing of birds – the turtle dove
(As when the first flood-waters fell away)
Will build her nest in the heart of the peaceful grove.

JOHN HEATH-STUBBS

THE PARABLE OF THE OLD MAN AND THE YOUNG

So Abram rose, and clave the wood, and went,
And took the fire with him, and a knife.
And as they sojourned both of them together,
Isaac the first-born spake and said, My Father,
Behold the preparations, fire and iron,

But where the lamb for this burnt-offering?
Then Abram bound the youth with belts and straps,
And builded parapets and trenches there,
And stretchèd forth the knife to slay his son.
When lo! an angel called him out of heaven,
Saying, Lay not thy hand upon the lad,
Neither do anything to him. Behold,
A ram, caught in a thicket by its horns;
Offer the Ram of Pride instead of him.
But the old man would not so, but slew his son,
And half the seed of Europe, one by one.

WILFRED OWEN

CHRIST AT GALLIPOLI

*This synod is convinced that the forces
of the Allies are being used of God to
vindicate the rights of the weak and to
maintain the moral order of the world.*
Anglican Synod, Melbourne, 1916.

Bit weird at first,
That starey look in the eyes,
The hair down past his shoulders,
But after a go with the ship's barber,
A sea-water shower and the old slouch hat
Across his ears, he started to look the part.
Took him a while to get the way
A bayonet fits the old Lee-Enfield,
But going in on the boats
He looked calmer than any of us,

213

Just gazing in over the swell
Where the cliffs looked black against the sky.
When we hit he fairly raced in through the waves,
Then up the beach, swerving like a full-back
    at the end
When the Turks'd really got on to us.
Time we all caught up,
He was off like a flash, up the cliffs,
After his first machine gun.
He'd done for three Turks when we got there,
The fourth was a gibbering mess.
Seeing him wave that blood–red bayonet,
I reckoned we were glad
To have him on the side.

GEOFF PAGE

SIGNS AND
SERVICES

FRESCOES IN AN OLD CHURCH*

Six centuries now have gone
Since, one by one,
These stones were laid,
And in air's vacancy
This beauty made.

They who thus reared them
Their long rest have won;
Ours now this heritage –
To guard, preserve, delight in, brood upon;
And in these transitory fragments scan
The immortal longings in the soul of Man.

WALTER DE LA MARE

*Stowell Park, Gloucestershire

PICTURE OF THE NATIVITY
IN THE CHURCH OF KRENA IN CHIOS

– Tell me, can this unsuspecting infant, staring
At the steep green sky, be 'He, who trampled upon
   Death'?
Everything round him is so poor and so untrue,
The brown ponies like shabby toys, the shepherds stilted
On their crooks, the Magi wooden kings that dare not
   bend,
Even the angels, village angels – they could never
Reach the sky again with those flat, clumsy wings.

– Silently, unawares and unbelievably come all
Great things: the inroad of great love, the mist of death.

CONSTANTINE TRYPANIS

IN CHURCH

The Church do seem a touching sight,
When folk a-coming in at door
Do softly tread the long-aisled floor
Below the pillared arches' height,
   With bells a-pealing,
   Folk a-kneeling,
Heart a-healing, wi' the love
An' peace a-sent 'em from above.

And there, wi' mild an' thoughtful face,
Wi' down-cast eyes and voices dumb,
The old and young do slowly come
And take in stillness each his place;
   A-sinking slowly
   Kneeling lowly,
Seeking holy thoughts alone
In prayer before their Maker's throne.

WILLIAM BARNES

A WISH

Mine be a cot beside the hill;
  A bee-hive's hum shall soothe my ear;
A willowy brook, that turns a mill,
  With many a fall shall linger near.

The swallow oft beneath my thatch
  Shall twitter from her clay-built nest;
Oft shall the pilgrim lift the latch
  And share my meal, a welcome guest.

Around my ivied porch shall spring
  Each fragrant flower that drinks the dew;
And Lucy at her wheel shall sing
  In russet gown and apron blue.

The village church among the trees,
  Where first our marriage vows were given,
With merry peals shall swell the breeze
  And point with taper spire to Heaven.

SAMUEL ROGERS

MASS AT DAWN

I dropped my sail and dried my dripping seines
Where the white quay is chequered by cool planes
In whose great branches, always out of sight,
The nightingales are singing day and night.
Though all was grey beneath the moon's grey beam,
My boat in her new paint shone like a bride,
And silver in my baskets shone the bream:
My arms were tired and I was heavy-eyed,
But when with food and drink, at morning-light,
The children met me at the water-side,
Never was wine so red or bread so white.

ROY CAMPBELL

ZULU EUCHARIST

The light that surrounds these faces
Is as tough as the soles of the feet
That, hardened to rhino hide
By running on thorns and rocky outcrops,
Chased the Imperial Army from Isandhlwana.

The sound of their hymns
Hammers at heaven like the thump-stamp of the war-
   dance.

Panic among the angels.
Hundreds and thousands
Of principalities, dominions and powers
Are taking crash courses in Zulu.

For the Zulu saints are running at Paradise
With the bull's-head roar of the charging impis,
And the sound of their songs and their laughter
Breaks on the shore
Like the great brown waves at the mouth
Of the crocodile-river Tugela.

LEO AYLEN

Isandhlwana, the 'Hill shaped like a little hand', was the site of the battle in
   1879 when the Zulu army wiped out a British regiment.
'Impi' is the word for a Zulu regiment. The famous Zulu military tactic was
   the 'bull's head' in which the wings became the 'horns' and encircled the
   enemy, while the great block of warriors – the 'head' – charged him
   head on.
The River Tugela is one of the boundaries of Zululand.
The nearest sound in a western language to the 'dhl' of 'Isandhlwana'
   is the Welsh 'll'.

FLYING BACK

They give us moistened BOAC towels
and I scrub my forehead. Red powder
for Holi: a trace of Delhi, an assault
met there in the wild streets this morning.
Without compunction I obliterate it –
India's not my country, let it go.
But crumpling the vermilion-stained napkin
(I shan't read it: some priest may do that)
I think of the stone foreheads in their hundreds:
Ganesh and Hanuman, who made me smile,
and Vishnu, and the four faces of Buddha,
reddened with genuine devotions;
and of the wooden cleft in a twisted tree
which I saw a beggar-woman sign scarlet
before she pressed her face down on to it;
and here's Nepal again. Sacred places
don't travel. The gods are stronger at home.
But if my tentative western brow may wear
this reluctant blush, these grains at the hair-roots,
I claim the right also to an image
as guardian; and choose winged Garuda.
His bland archaic countenance beams out
that serenity to which I journey.

FLEUR ADCOCK

COMINGS AND GOINGS

FOR A CHILD EXPECTED

Lovers whose lifted hands are candles in winter,
Whose gentle ways like streams in the easy summer,
Lying together
For secret setting of a child, love what they do,
Thinking they make that candle immortal, those streams
   forever flow,
And yet do better than they know.

So the first flutter of a baby felt in the womb,
Its little signal and promise of riches to come,
Is taken in its father's name;
Its life is the body of his love, like his caress,
First delicate and strange, that daily use
Makes dearer and priceless.

Our baby was to be the living sign of our joy,
Restore to each the other's lost infancy;
To a painter's pillaging eye
Poet's coiled hearing, add the heart we might earn
By the help of love; all that our passion would yield
We put to planning our child.

The world flowed in; whatever we liked we took:
For its hair, the gold curls of the November oak
We saw on our walk;
Snowberries that make a Milky Way in the wood
For its tender hands; calm screen of the frozen flood
For our care of its childhood.

But the birth of a child is an uncontrollable glory;
Cat's cradle of hopes will hold no living baby,
Long though it lay quietly.

And when our baby stirs and struggles to be born
It compels humility: what we began
Is now its own.

For *as the sun that shines through glass*
So Jesus in His Mother was.
Therefore every human creature,
Since it shares in His nature,
In candle-gold passion or white
Sharp star should show its own way of light.
May no parental dread or dream
Darken our darling's early beam:
May she grow to her right powers
Unperturbed by passion of ours.

ANNE RIDLER

THE EVIL EYE

The belief in the Evil Eye is a still-surviving superstition
among Italian country people. One method of detecting its
presence is to pour olive oil on a saucer of holy water. The
shapes assumed by the oil can then be read by the gifted.

Nona poured oil on the water and saw the eye
    Form on my birth. Zia beat me with bay,
    Fennel, and barley to scourge the devil away.
I doubt I needed so much excuse to cry.

From Sister Maria Immaculata there came
    A crucifix, a vow of nine days' prayer,
    And a scapular stitched with virgin's hair.
The eye glowed on the water all the same.

By Felice, the midwife, I was hung with a tin
   Fish stuffed with garlic and bread crumbs.
   Three holy waters washed the breast for my gums.
Still the eye glared, wide as original sin,

On the deepest pools of women midnight-spoken
   To ward my clamoring soul from the clutch of hell,
   Lest growing I be no comfort and dying swell
More than a grave with horror. Still unbroken

The eye glared through the roosts of all their clucking.
   'Jesu,' cried Mother, 'why is he deviled so?'
   'Baptism without delay,' said Father Cosmo.
'This one is not for sprinkling but for ducking.'

So in came meat and wine and the feast was on.
   I wore a palm frond in my lace, and sewn
   To my swaddling band a hoop and three beads of bone
For the Trinity. And they ducked me and called me
   John.

And ate the meat and drank the wine, and the eye
   Closed on the water. All this fell between
   My first scream and first name in 1916,
The year of the war and the influenza, when I

Was not yet ready for evil or my own name,
Though I had one already and the other came.

JOHN CIARDI

scapular: small cloth badge worn on string around the neck by devout
   Roman Catholics

THE NEED FOR BAPTISM

You can't dress
     in cloth
          come straight from the loom.
First it's fulled
     trampled underfoot
          beaten
With mallets
     cleansed
          and its texture thickened.
Then it's rinsed
     cleaner still
          combed with teazles
Stretched
     on tenterhooks
          by the tailor's hand.
     It's the same with a newborn baby.
     Till it's baptized in the name of Christ,
     Confirmed, by the bishop, it's heathen
     In heaven's sight and its soul helpless.
The word 'heathen'
     comes from 'heath'
          untilled ground.
There, in the waste places
     wild beasts
          rampage
And breed untamed
     running loose
          untrammelled.

WILLIAM LANGLAND

(from *The Vision of Piers Plowman*, translated from the Middle English
by Ronald Tamplin)

227

EARLY MORNING FEED

The father darts out on the stairs
To listen to the keening
In the upper room, for a change of note
That signifies distress, to scotch disaster,
The kettle humming in the room behind.

He thinks, on tiptoe, ears a-strain,
The cool dawn rising like the moon:
'Must not appear and pick him up;
He mustn't think he has me springing
To his beck and call,'
The kettle rattling behind the kitchen door.

He has him springing
A-quiver on the landing –
For a distress-note, a change of key,
To gallop up the stairs to him
To take him up, light as a violin,
And stroke his back until he smiles.
He sidles in the kitchen
And pours his tea . . .

And again stands hearkening
For milk cracking the lungs.
There's a little panting,
A cough: the thumb's in: he'll sleep,
The cup of tea cooling on the kitchen table.

Can he go in now to his chair and think
Of the miracle of breath, pick up a book,
Ready at all times to take it at a run

And intervene between him and disaster,
Sipping his cold tea as the sun comes up?

He returns to bed
And feels like something, with the door ajar,
Crouched in the bracken, alert, with big eyes
For the hunter, death, disaster.

PETER REDGROVE

BIRTH OF RAINBOW

This morning blue vast clarity of March sky
But a blustery violence of air, and a soaked overnight
Newpainted look to the world. The wind coming
Off the snowed moor in the South, razorish,
Heavy-bladed and head-cutting, off snow-powdered
   ridges.
Flooded ruts shook. Hoof-puddles flashed. A daisy
Mud-plastered unmixed its head from the mud.
The black and white cow, on the highest crest of the
   round ridge,
Stood under the end of a rainbow.
Head down licking something, full in the painful wind
That the pouring haze of the rainbow ignored.
She was licking her gawky black calf
Collapsed wet-fresh from the womb, blinking his eyes
In the low morning dazzling washed sun.
Black, wet as a collie from a river, as she licked him,
Finding his smells, learning his particularity.
A flag of bloody tissue hung from her back-end

Spreading and shining, pink-fleshed and raw, it flapped
   and coiled
In the unsparing wind. She positioned herself, uneasy
As we approached, nervous small footwork
On the hoof-ploughed drowned sod of the ruined field.
She made uneasy low noises, and her calf too
With his staring whites, mooed the full clear calf-note
Pure as woodwind, and tried to get up,
Tried to get his cantilever front legs
In operation, lifted his shoulders, hoisted to his knees,
Then hoisted his back end and lurched forward
On his knees and crumpling ankles, sliding in the mud
And collapsing plastered. She went on licking him.
She started eating the banner of thin raw flesh that
Spinnakered from her rear. We left her to it.
Blobbed antiseptic on to the sodden blood-dangle
Of his muddy birth-cord, and left her
Inspecting the new smell. The whole South West
Was black as nightfall.
Trailing squall-smokes hung over the moor leaning
And whitening towards us, then the world blurred
And disappeared in forty-five degree hail
And a gate-jerking blast. We got to cover.
Left to God the calf and his mother.

TED HUGHES

THE BORDER

What shall avail me
When I reach the border?
This staff will fail me,
This pass all in order.

These words I have learned
Will not help me then,
These honours hard earned,
And applause of men.

My harp truly set
Will break string by string;
I shall quite forget
That once I could sing.

Absence pure and cold
Of sense and memory
Lightly will hold
All that is me.

All, all will fail me,
Tongue, foot and hand.
Strange I shall hale me
To that strange land.

EDWIN MUIR

SAINT CADOC

A flame of rushlight in the cell
On holy walls and holy well
And to the west the thundering bay
With soaking seaweed, sand and spray,
  Oh good St Cadoc pray for me
  Here in your cell beside the sea.

Somewhere the tree, the yellowing oak,
Is waiting for the woodman's stroke,
Waits for the chisel saw and plane
To prime it for the earth again
  And in the earth, for me inside,
  The generous oak tree will have died.

St Cadoc blest the woods of ash
Bent landwards by the Western lash,
He loved the veinèd threshold stones
Where sun might sometime bleach his bones
  He had no cowering fear of death
  For breath of God was Cadoc's breath.

Some cavern generates the germs
To send my body to the worms,
To-day some red hands make the shell
To blow my soul away to Hell
  To-day a pair walks newly married
  Along the path where I'll be carried.

St Cadoc, when the wind was high,
Saw angels in the Cornish sky
As ocean rollers curled and poured
Their loud Hosannas to the Lord,

His little cell was not too small
For that great Lord who made them all.

Here where St Cadoc sheltered God
The archaeologist has trod,
Yet death is now the gentle shore
With Land upon the cliffs before
　　And in his cell beside the sea
　　The Celtic saint has prayed for me.

SIR JOHN BETJEMAN

Cadoc, the great sixth-century Welsh missionary-saint, is believed to have
visited Cornwall. The site of an ancient chapel and Holy Well named
after him is to be found near Harlyn Bay, on the north Cornish coast.

AT THE GRAVE OF HENRY VAUGHAN

Above the voiceful windings of a river
An old green slab of simply graven stone
Shuns notice, overshadowed by a yew.
Here Vaughan lies dead, whose name flows on for ever
Through pastures of the spirit washed with dew
And starlit with eternities unknown.

Here sleeps the Silurist; the loved physician;
The face that left no portraiture behind;
The skull that housed white angels and had vision
Of daybreak through the gateways of the mind.

233

Here faith and mercy, wisdom and humility
(Whose influence shall prevail for evermore)
Shine. And this lowly grave tells Heaven's
    tranquillity.
And here stand I, a suppliant at the door.

SIEGFRIED SASSOON

Silurist: Vaughan, known as the 'Silurist', was born in Brecknockshire, a
  place he grew to love deeply, and which is a district of south-east Wales
  once inhabited (among other areas) by the Silures, an ancient British
  tribe

MASS

When the battle was over
and the fighter was dead, a man approached him
and said, 'Don't die, I love you so!'
But the corpse, alas, kept dying.

Two came up to him and repeated,
'Don't leave us! Take heart, come back to life!'
But the corpse, alas, kept dying.

Twenty ran up to him, a hundred, a thousand, five
    hundred thousand,
crying out, 'So much love and to be powerless against
    death!'
But the corpse, alas, kept dying.

Millions of individuals surrounded him
with a common petition, 'Hold on, brother!'

But the corpse, alas, kept dying.

Then all men on earth
surrounded him; the sad corpse saw them and was
    moved;
he sat up slowly,
embraced the first man and started to walk . . .

CÉSAR VALLEJO
(translated from the Spanish by
Charles Guenther)

ON ALL SOULS' DAY

Last night they lit your glass with wine
And brought for you the sweet soul-cake,
And blessed the room with candle-shine
For the grave journey you would make.

They told me not to stir between
The midnight strokes of one and two,
And I should see you come again
To view the scene that once you knew.

'Good night,' they said, and journeyed on.
I turned the key, and – turning – smiled,
And in the quiet house alone
I slept serenely as a child.

Innocent was that sleep, and free,
And when the first of morning shone
I had no need to gaze and see
If crumb, or bead of wine, had gone.

My heart was easy as this bloom
Of waters rising by the bay.
I did not watch where you might come,
For you had never been away.
For you have never been away.

CHARLES CAUSLEY

THE LITTLE AIRCRAFT

The little aircraft trudging through night, cloud, rain,
Is neither alone nor lost among the great
Inverted ocean of the air, for a lane
Invisible gives it intelligence,
The crossing needles keep its heading right,
The neutrally numbering voices of its friends
Make of its blindness blind obedience,
From one to another handing its destiny on
The stages of the way with course and height
Till finally it's funneled in and down
Over the beacons along the narrowing beam,
Perfectly trusting a wisdom not its own,
That breaking out of cloud it may be come
Back to this world and be born again,
Into the valley of the flarepath, fallen home.

HOWARD NEMEROV

WONDER

How like an angel came I down!
  How bright are all things here!
When first among his works I did appear,
  Oh, how their Glory me did crown!
The world resembled his Eternity,
    In which my soul did walk;
  And every thing that I did see
    Did with me talk.

The skies in their magnificence,
  The lively, lovely air;
Oh, how divine, how soft, how sweet, how fair!
  The stars did entertain my sense,
And all the works of God so bright and pure,
    So rich and great did seem
  As if they ever must endure
    In my esteem.

A native health and innocence
  Within my bones did grow,
And while my God did all his glories show,
  I felt a vigour in my sense
That was all spirit. I within did flow
  With seas of life, like wine;
  I nothing in the world did know,
    But 'twas divine.

Harsh, ragged objects were concealed,
  Oppressions, tears, and cries,
Sins, griefs, complaints, dissentions, weeping eyes,
  Were hid: and only things revealed

237

Which heavenly spirits and the angels prize.
 The State of Innocence
And Bliss, not trades and poverties,
 Did fill my sense.

The streets were paved with golden stones,
 The boys and girls were mine;
Oh, how did all their lovely faces shine!
The Sons of Men were Holy Ones,
Joy, Beauty, Welfare did appear to me,
 And every thing which here I found,
While like an angel I did see,
 Adorned the ground.

Rich diamond, and pearl, and gold
 In every place was seen;
Rare splendours, yellow, blue, red, white, and green,
 Mine eyes did everywhere behold;
Great Wonders clothed with Glory did appear,
 Amazement was my Bliss.
That and my wealth was everywhere:
 No Joy to this . . .

THOMAS TRAHERNE

INDEX OF FIRST LINES

239

INDEX OF AUTHORS

ACKNOWLEDGEMENTS

The editor and publishers gratefully acknowledge permission to reproduce copyright material in this collection.

FLEUR ADCOCK: From *The Scenic Route* © Oxford University Press 1974. Reprinted by permission of Oxford University Press. ALCUIN: From *Mediaeval Latin Lyrics*, translated by Helen Waddell. Reprinted by permission of Constable Publishers. W. H. AUDEN: From *Collected Shorter Poems*. Reprinted by permission of Faber & Faber Ltd. LEO AYLEN: From *Return to Zululand*. Reprinted by permission of Sidgwick & Jackson Ltd. MICHAEL BALDWIN: From *Hob and other Poems*. Reprinted by permission of the author and Chatto & Windus Ltd. EDITH C. BATHO: 'As Mary Was A-Walking' and 'St Joseph and God's Mother' by permission of the translator. FRANCES BELLERBY: From *Selected Poems* (Enitharmon Press). By permission of the copyright holder. HILAIRE BELLOC: From *Collected Poems*. Reprinted by permission of A. D. Peters & Co. Ltd. JOHN BETJEMAN: From *Collected Poems*. Reprinted by permission of John Murray (Publishers) Ltd. THOMAS BLACKBURN: 'Jonah' from *The Outer Darkness*, 'Hospital for Defectives' from *The Next Word*. By permission of Mrs Peggy Blackburn. GEORGE MACKAY BROWN: From *Fishermen with Ploughs*. Reprinted by permission of the author and The Hogarth Press. ROY CAMPBELL: From *Collected Poems* (The Bodley Head Ltd). Reprinted by permission of Curtis Brown Ltd on behalf of the Estate of Roy Campbell. CHARLES CAUSLEY: From *Collected Poems* (Macmillan). Reprinted by permission of David Higham Associates Ltd. G. K. CHESTERTON: From *Collected Poems*. Reprinted by permission of A. P. Watt Ltd on behalf of The Estate of G. K. Chesterton and J. M. Dent & Sons Ltd. JOHN CIARDI: From *As If*. Copyright © John Ciardi 1955. By permission of the author. LEONARD CLARK: From *Secret as Toads*. Reprinted by permission of the author and Chatto & Windus Ltd. JACK CLEMO: From *The Echoing Tip*. Reprinted by permission of Methuen & Co. Ltd. WALTER DE LA MARE: From *Complete Poems*. Reprinted by permission of The Literary Trustees of Walter de la Mare and The Society of Authors as their representative. W. H. DAVIES: From *Complete Poems of W. H. Davies*. Reprinted by permission of the Executors of the W. H. Davies Estate and Jonathan Cape Ltd. NORMA DOUGLAS-HENRY: 'A Ballad of St John's Morning' by permission of the translator. T. S. ELIOT: From *Murder in the Cathedral*. Reprinted by permission of Faber & Faber Ltd. D. J. ENRIGHT: From *The Terrible Shears*. Reprinted by permission of Bolt & Watson Ltd. GAVIN EWART: By permission of the author.

245

ACKNOWLEDGEMENTS

'Prayer' first appeared in the *Listener*. ELEANOR FARJEON: From *Silver Sand and Snow*. Reprinted by permission of David Higham Associates Ltd and Michael Joseph Ltd. ROBERT FROST: From *The Poetry of Robert Frost*, ed. Edward Connery Lathem, Copyright 1942 by Robert Frost, Copyright © 1969 by Holt, Rinehart & Winston, Copyright © 1970 by Lesley Frost Ballantine. Reprinted by permission of the Estate of Robert Frost, Jonathan Cape Ltd, and Holt, Rinehart & Winston. CHRISTOPHER FRY: From *The Boy with a Cart*. Copyright © Christopher Fry. Reprinted by permission of Frederick Muller Ltd, London. KAREN GERSHON: From *Coming Back From Babylon*. Reprinted by permission of Victor Gollancz Ltd. RUMER GODDEN: From *St Jerome and the Lion*. Reprinted by permission of Macmillan London and Basingstoke. ROBERT GRAVES: From *Ann at Highwood Hall*. Reprinted by permission of A. P. Watt Ltd on behalf of Mr Robert Graves. THOMAS HARDY: From *Collected Poems* (Macmillan London and Basingstoke). SEAMUS HEANEY: From *Death of a Naturalist*. Reprinted by permission of Faber & Faber Ltd. JOHN HEATH-STUBBS: 'The Hundred and Thirty-seventh Psalm Paraphrased', 'The Storm Petrel', 'The House Sparrow', 'The Peacock and the Snake', 'The Kingfisher', 'The Hoopoe' from *A Charm Against the Tooth Ache*. Reprinted by permission of the author and Eyre-Methuen Ltd. 'The History of the Flood' from *The Blue-Fly in His Head*. Reprinted by permission of the author and Oxford University Press. 'The Turtle Dove' from *A Parliament of Birds*. Reprinted by permission of the author and Chatto & Windus Ltd. ZBIGNIEW HERBERT: 'The Seventh Angel' from *Selected Poems*, trans. Czeslaw Milosz and Peter Dale Scott (Penguin Modern European Poets, 1968, pp. 51–2). Translation copyright © Czeslaw Milosz and Peter Dale Scott, 1968. Reprinted by permission of Penguin Books Ltd. GERARD MANLEY HOPKINS: From *The Poems of Gerard Manley Hopkins*, 4th edition, ed. W. H. Gardner and N. H. MacKenzie (Oxford University Press). TED HUGHES: 'Birth of Rainbow' from *Moortown*. 'New Year Song' from *Season's Songs*. Reprinted by permission of Faber and Faber Ltd. MAURICE HUSSEY: From *The Chester Cycle of Miracle Plays*, trans. Maurice Hussey. Reprinted by permission of Heinemann Educational Books. ELIZABETH JENNINGS: From *Collected Poems*. Reprinted by permission of the author and Macmillan London Ltd. JAMES WELDON JOHNSON: 'The Creation' from *God's Trombones*. Copyright 1927 by The Viking Press, Inc. Copyright renewed © 1955 by Grace Nail Johnson. Reprinted by permission of Viking Penguin Inc. PATRICK KAVANAGH: From *Collected Poems* (MacGibbon & Kee). By permission of Mrs P. Kavanagh. JAMES KIRKUP: From *A Refusal to Conform*. By permission of the author. WILLIAM LANGLAND: From *The Vision of Piers Plowman*, trans. Ronald Tamplin. By permission of the translator.

ACKNOWLEDGEMENTS

PETER LEVI: From *The Gravel Ponds* (1960). Reprinted by permission of André Deutsch Ltd. SAMUEL MENASHE: From *To Open*. By permission of the author. JOHN MASEFIELD: Reprinted by permission of The Society of Authors as the literary representative of the Estate of John Masefield. EDWIN MUIR: From *The Collected Poems of Edwin Muir*. Reprinted by permission of Faber & Faber Ltd. LES MURRAY: From *The Weatherboard Cathedral*. Copyright © Les A. Murray, 1969. Reprinted by permission of Angus & Robertson (U.K.) Ltd. HOWARD NEMEROV: From *Sentences* (The University of Chicago Press, 1980). Reprinted by permission of the author. NORMAN NICHOLSON: 'The Burning Bush' from *Five Rivers*. Reprinted by permission of Faber & Faber Ltd. 'A Local Preacher's Goodbye' from *A Local Habitation*. Reprinted by permission of the author and Faber & Faber Ltd. JOHN NORMANTON: Reprinted from *The London Magazine*, by permission of the author. PHILIP OAKES: From *In the Affirmative* (1968). Reprinted by permission of André Deutsch Ltd. WILFRED OWEN: From the *Collected Poems of Wilfred Owen*, ed. C. Day-Lewis. Reprinted by permission of The Owen Estate and Chatto & Windus Ltd. GEOFF PAGE: From *Small Town Memorials* (1975). Reprinted by permission of University of Queensland Press. KATHLEEN RAINE: From *Collected Poems*. Reprinted by permission of George Allen & Unwin. PETER REDGROVE: From *The Collector and Other Poems* (1959). Reprinted by permission of Routledge & Kegan Paul Ltd. ANNE RIDLER: From *The Nine Bright Shiners* (Faber & Faber). By permission of the author. SIEGFRIED SASSOON: From *Collected Poems*. Reprinted by permission of Mr G. T. Sassoon. VERNON SCANNELL: From *The Winter Man*. Reprinted by permission of Allison & Busby Ltd. GOH POH SENG: From *Eyewitness*. © Goh Poh Seng. Reprinted by permission of the author and Heinemann Educational Books (Asia) Ltd. THOMAS W. SHAPCOTT: By permission of the author. JAMES STEPHENS: From *Collected Poems*. Reprinted by permission of Mrs Iris Wise and Macmillan London and Basingstoke. L. A. G. STRONG: From *The Body's Imperfection*. Reprinted by permission of Methuen & Co. Ltd. RONALD TAMPLIN: By permission of the author. R. S. THOMAS: From *Young and Old*. Reprinted by permission of Granada Publishing Ltd. CONSTANTINE TRYPANIS: From *The Stones of Troy*. Reprinted by permission of Faber & Faber Ltd. CESAR VALLEJO: From *Modern European Poetry*, ed. Willis Barnstone (Bantam Books). This translation by permission of Charles Guenther. JOHN WAIN: From *Weep Before God*. Reprinted by permission of Curtis Brown Ltd. on behalf of John Wain and Macmillan London and Basingstoke. JUDITH WRIGHT: 'Five Senses' from *Selected Poems*. Copyright © Judith Wright, 1963. Reprinted by permission of Angus & Robertson (U.K.) Ltd. W. B. YEATS: From *Collected Poems*.

ACKNOWLEDGEMENTS

Reprinted by permission of A. P. Watt Ltd on behalf of M. B. Yeats, Anne Yeats and Macmillan London Ltd.

'Evening' by Thomas Miller, 'The Ten Commandments' (anon. 1731) and 'The Tower of Babel' by Nathaniel Crouch from *The Oxford Book of Children's Verse*, ed. Iona and Peter Opie, 1973 (Oxford University Press).

'Mary's Wandering', 'Easter Eggs' trans. P. Dearmer, 'Mothering Sunday' by George Hare Leonard, 'The Merchants' Carol' by Frank Kendon, 'Thanksgiving Carol' by Eleanor Farjeon, from *The Oxford Book of Carols*. Reprinted by permission of Oxford University Press. 'All in the Morning', 'May Carol', 'The Miraculous Harvest' and 'A New Dial', all collated by Percy Dearmer, from *The Oxford Book of Carols*.

W. H. AUDEN: From *The Play of Daniel*, ed. by Noah Greenberg, Narration by W. H. Auden. Narration © 1958 by W. H. Auden. Reprinted by permission of Oxford University Press, Inc.

Every effort has been made to trace copyright holders but if any omissions have been made please let us know and acknowledgements will be made in the next edition.